JUST FOR GIRLS

FACILITATOR'S MANUAL

A program to help girls safely navigate
the rocky road through adolescence
and avoid pitfalls such as
eating disorders and
the preoccupation
with food and
weight.

by
Sandra Susan Friedman
BA, BSW, MA

SALAL BOOKS

Vancouver
British Columbia
Canada

Text editing, graphic design, layout and DTP production: Dan Fivehouse/SALAL COMMUNICATIONS LTD.

Printed by: FRIESENS of Altona, Manitoba, Canada

Canadian Cataloguing in Publication Data

Friedman, Sandra Susan, 1942-
  Just for girls

  Previous ed. has title: Girls in the 90s
  Includes bibliographic references
  ISBN 0-9698883-1-7

  1. Girls—Counseling of. 2. Girls—Psychology. 3. Body image in adolesence. 4. Eating disorders. I. Title. II. Title: Girls in the 90s.
HQ798.F744 1999   305.235   C99-910066-1

First publication January 1999

ACKNOWLEDGMENTS

JUST FOR GIRLS has been greatly enriched by the contributions of many generous people. Colleen Penner Podaima and Shirley Fineblit provided me with thoughtful and insightful feedback about the manuscript. Czesia Fuks Geddes piqued my interest in depression with books, articles and resources. Cindy Rammage spent time sharing her experiences with the *Girls in the 90s* groups and gave me copies of some of her resources that I then adapted for this book. Mary Lynn Jardine sent me a Journal that she created for her grade six groups. Sharon Young provided me with a list of videos. Marcus Youssef of *Safe Teen* shared his experiences about working with boys. Tammy Lawrence of *Promotion Plus* kept me supplied with new program resources for girls, while Cathy Ellsmere and Nicki Breuer of *Odin Books* once again made sure that my reading list was up to date.

My heartfelt thanks goes to the many facilitators who provided me with feedback about their groups and with suggestions for topics that I might include in this book. They include Anne Cartin, Kathy Banks, Nancy McAlary, Jo-Anne Doucet, Catherine Berry, Jan Bainbridge, Karen Emery, Lynne Alton, Judy Rollier, Wendy Shaeffer, Faith Thomson, Rhonda Userik, Marilyn Lemon, Barb Douglas, Lori Dobud, Jill Thompson, Debbie Reid, Marie-Josee Perrault, Judy DeRoose and Connie Nixon.

I would like to express my appreciation for Dr. Lorna Medd, the godmother of the original *Girls in the 90s* program, for her continuous support of my work and for her contribution to eating disorder prevention in British Columbia. Many thanks to my friends Louise Doyle, Marion Crook and Carol Herbert for acting as sounding boards throughout this project.

Finally, I would like to express my love and appreciation for my husband, friend and professional partner, Dan Fivehouse, for encouraging me in my work with girls and eating disorder prevention, and for his superb job of editing my papers and my books.

TABLE OF CONTENTS

INTRODUCTION

A group of girls saunters down a hallway. They jostle each other and giggle as girls are apt to do. The lilt and cadence of their adolescent voices drift through the air punctuated by shrieks of 'awesome,' 'totally,' and 'cool.' The girls are excited because they are all participants in a *JUST FOR GIRLS* group—an eating disorder prevention program where they can engage in *girl talk* and share their issues, fears, laughter and concerns.

❈   ❈   ❈

It is impossible to grow up female today without every worrying about weight, without sometimes apologizing for eating or restricting what you eat or without 'feeling fat.' Six and seven year old girls express concern with how they look. Nine year old girls talk about wanting to be thinner even before their bodies have begun to change. When girls are ten and eleven years old and have begun to go through puberty, most of them will tell you that they 'feel fat.' No matter how many times we tell girls that people come in a range of sizes and that the shape of their bodies is really determined by their genes, it's hard for them to take us seriously. Girls are seduced by relentless messages from the culture that everyone wants to be thin, that being thin automatically endows you with perfection and eternal confidence and that they can change their bodies if they try hard enough.

While most girls worry about their weight, not all girls worry to the same extent and not everybody develops an eating disorder. However, 'feeling fat' and worrying about weight extracts a high price from girls. It affects their self-esteem, their relationships with others and their performance in school. It also affects their health. The same societal conditions that encourage girls to define themselves by the numbers on the scale will also make them vulnerable to other risks that stem from a lack of connection to their selves and their bodies—such as depression, smoking, teen pregnancy and sexually transmitted diseases.

In 1992 I had the opportunity to develop an eating disorder prevention program for girls. The project drew upon a lifetime of different professional skills and personal experiences. They began when I was an elementary and then high school teacher with an uneasy relationship with food. When I went back to university later on, the MA in psychology that I received provided me with insights into my own issues regarding body image and weight, and valuable counseling skills. It gave me a societal context that helped me understand why so many other women like myself were preoccupied with food and weight. It also launched my career as a therapist. I spent the next fifteen years helping women with disordered eating and with eating disorders identify and resolve the underlying issues and take charge of their lives. In shifting my focus to prevention—and especially to addressing the concerns of adolescent girls—my professional and personal life had come full-circle. I was once again involved with the elementary/middle school system where I had begun. However, instead of worrying about my weight, I was working with girls so that they would not worry about theirs.

Developing a prevention program was no easy task. It involved a lot of trial-by-error work, as well as learning to listen carefully to girls' voices—even when I was sure I knew best. It meant understanding that prevention has little to do with eating disorders and the behaviors associated with them and a lot to do with addressing what happens to girls in the process of growing up female that makes them feel fat. Developing a prevention program meant taking the focus off food and weight and instead addressing the realities of girls' lives and experiences as they made the transition through adolescence into the adult world. As the girls themselves said, 'Even if we sometimes worry about our body image and self-confidence—that's not what it's about. It's about what we do and what we want—all the things that concern us as girls.' And so the *Girls in the 90s* discussion group program was born.

As *Girls in the 90s* developed a life and momentum of its own I was inundated by requests from mothers who wanted something more comprehensive by way of background information for themselves and skills they could use with their daughters. In response I wrote *When Girls Feel Fat: Helping Girls Through Adolescence* which was published in May of 1997. To my delight the book became popular not only with parents and professionals but also with adolescent girls. In order to promote the book (and because I love to speak) I conducted over 50 public seminars and professional training workshops in Canada and the United States. As I traveled from coast to coast, I spoke to thousands of mothers, fathers, adolescent girls and professionals about why girls feel fat and about the experience of being an adolescent girl today. I listened to the concerns of parents and answered questions from girls about their bodies and their friendships, their relationships with boys and their emotional lives. I heard about the experiences of many women who had facilitated *Girls in the 90s* groups.

With the year 2000 quickly approaching the time had come to change the name of the program to *JUST FOR GIRLS*. This gave me the opportunity to integrate the past five years of experiences, the new ideas I had accumulated along the way and the feedback from group facilitators and girls into this new improved facilitator's manual. While I added lots of new material to this book, I have tried hard to avoid duplicating the information presented in *When Girls Feel Fat*.

JUST FOR GIRLS is a prevention program for adolescent girls. It is based on a belief that disordered eating, eating disorders, depression and the other health and social risks that girls face are coping mechanisms that they develop in order to deal with the changes in their lives and bodies as they grow up female in a primarily male-defined world. The core of the program is an open discussion group that looks at what feeling fat means to girls and addresses this dynamic before it can become a fixed (or internalized) way for them to respond to situations in their lives—or escalate into dieting and other disordered eating and eating disorder behaviors.

JUST FOR GIRLS teaches girls to recognize the *grungies*—a term coined to describe the negative voice that girls develop as they grow up. While the most common *grungie* is feeling fat, feeling stupid and feeling ugly are close behind. The program help girls recognize when they have been hit by a *grungie* and encourages them to talk about what else was happening to them at the time—to tell the real stories that lie underneath. In this way *JUST FOR GIRLS* addresses the silencing of girls' voices in adolescence and their subsequent loss of self.

JUST FOR GIRLS helps girls understand why they feel the way that they do by reframing their stories in terms of female development and culture. Girls march to a different drummer than boys do. Even though they participate in the same activities as boys, many girls will do them and describe them differently. The program helps girls understand the societal pressures that they face during adolescence and how these contribute to the changes in their lives. It helps girls understand the physical and emotional changes they experience during puberty and provides them with an awareness of their own bodies that goes beyond relating to them solely in terms of how they look. It teaches girls how to strengthen their friendships and support one another and thus celebrates their interdependence with the relevant people in their lives and highlights the importance of those relationships to them.

The *JUST FOR GIRLS* book provides you with everything you need to know to set up and facilitate a *JUST FOR GIRLS* group. It explains the philosophy underlying the program and gives you information about eating disorders and depression (the biggest health risks to girls) so that you can recognize the warning signs and find the appropriate resources for girls at risk. It provides you with a blueprint for the group process, background information about the topics, and activities and handouts that you can use for each session. The next section entitled HOW TO USE THIS BOOK provides an overview of the program and describes the interconnected sections.

The *JUST FOR GIRLS* book provides you with information about male development and culture and about working with boys. It contains suggestions about how you can enrich your relationships with boys and about how you can help male group leaders develop resources appropriate to the male gender culture.

The *JUST FOR GIRLS* program is designed for use by women of different orientations and levels of experience. You don't need four PhDs and three training programs to facilitate a group. What you need the most is a willingness to share yourself (and if possible a co-facilitator to share the experience with), a lot of curiosity and the ability to listen to the voices of the girls. The best way for you and the girls to learn is by doing—through trial and error. The session plans can help you structure your weekly groups until you are comfortable enough to do so yourself. If something doesn't work the first time, try something else. Pick and choose among the session plans and activities that you relate to most comfortably, and which best address the concerns of the girls you are working with. Adapt them to your own style and to the needs of your group.

As facilitators have told me over and over again, the best part of the program is the opportunity that they receive to learn about the girls and to contribute to their growth. For the girls the most valuable part is always the opportunity to talk about their concerns and to know that other girls feel the same way. In the end, that is what matters most.

HOW TO USE THIS BOOK

This book has been written for women who are interested in working with pre-adolescent and adolescent girls in a group setting—women who have a degree of curiosity about themselves, and a willingness to share their life experiences and knowledge. A sense of humor helps as well! This book is designed to be used, and used often. It is best to read through it the first time in the order presented. If you find that some of the material repeats itself, that is because the book is made up of interconnected sections which can be combined or used separately:

CULTURE will provide you with the basis for understanding the philosophy behind the *JUST FOR GIRLS* program. It describes how girls and boys develop and grow up in two separate gender cultures with different languages and different ways of responding to the world. It looks at how gender differences begin in the brain and at the effect that psychological development and societal influence have on behavior.

ADOLESCENCE looks at what happens to girls when they have to deny their own culture in order to fit into the male world. This section includes information about eating disorders and depression—the two major health risks for girls. While you don't have to be a specialist in these areas to facilitate a *JUST FOR GIRLS* group, it helps to understand them in the context of the girls' lives and experiences and to know when girls are at risk.

CORE provides you with everything that you need to know to set-up and facilitate your own program. CORE explains the goals of the program and provides a blueprint which you can adapt to your own interests and to the interests and appropriate age of the girls in your group. It explores what we as women bring to the process of working with girls. It looks at our connection to the girls, at their connections with each other, and our role in helping them become resources for one another. It also describes the role of the school in helping girls make a healthy transition through adolescence.

CONTEXT provides a societal and developmental context for the issues that the girls raise in the groups, and the experiences that they describe. This section provides you with a menu of *learning activities* for each topic that you can use to provoke discussion or to deepen awareness.

JUST FOR BOYS provides you with an understanding of male development and male culture, and explains what happens to boys as they make the transition through adolescence. It describes the kinds of programs and strategies that are congruent with male culture and explores what men bring to the process of working with boys.

RESOURCES lists books, programs, magazines and videos that can help you and the girls develop a deeper understanding of the topics.

SESSION PLANS will help you design your groups. You can use them as is, mix & match them, adapt them to suit the particular needs of your group or ignore them.

REPRODUCIBLE HANDOUTS provide you with information and activities that you can use in your sessions.

Once you have familiarized yourself with the program, use the book as a general reference for working with girls. It will serve as a guide to help you answer specific questions about the things that are of concern to them, to assist you in learning more about preventing the risks to which girls are vulnerable, and to broaden your own perspective about what it is like to grow up female in a male world. My book *When Girls Feel Fat* contains information in greater detail relating to each of these subjects.

The *JUST FOR GIRLS* program is designed to be facilitated by women with varied personal and professional experiences and orientations. The focus of the particular group will depend upon the needs of the girls and upon your own comfort level. Remember that the most important thing that you bring to the group is *yourself*.

CULTURE

Two babies lie sleeping in their carriers. 'Look how cute and delicate Jennifer is,' boast her parents. 'She's so quiet. We've never seen such a good baby.' 'Michael lets us know what he wants,' his parents proudly exclaim. 'He's so strong and sturdy. He's going to be some guy!'

The influence of gender

Gender has a profound influence upon us from birth. Though these babies are barely one month old, the fact that they are differentiated as female and male respectively has already begun to play a major role in shaping their lives. Adults will handle and treat them each differently depending upon their perception of the baby's gender.

Gender socialization determines what we are named and how we are treated, the clothes that we will wear, what toys we will be given and the games that we will play. It molds us into what society defines as masculine and feminine. It teaches us how to act and behave separately as girls and boys, and later as women or men. It instructs us in the different roles that we are thus expected or required to play. As we mature, gender socialization will influence the kinds of jobs we will have and the amount of money that we will get paid for doing them. Factors such as our race, ethnicity and socio-economic class will reinforce these differing standards of behavior for us as girls and boys, and women and men. So too will our relatives, friends, childcare workers, school and institutional officials, employers, the media and our peers influence and reinforce these differences.

Some people believe that gender differences are only the result of socialization, and therefore what is learned can be unlearned. Yet despite their efforts to treat boys and girls the same, little boys make guns out of dolls and little girls relate to their trucks as family—with the large truck as the daddy, the middle truck as the mommy, and the rest of the trucks as babies. The notion that we can narrow the 'gender gap' between them by teaching girls competitive sports and encouraging boys to be more sensitive doesn't begin to address the fundamental differences in the ways in which girls and boys experience and respond to the world.

1.

Girls and boys inhabit two distinct gender cultures with quite different languages and different ways of interpreting and responding to situations. While they may as individuals do the exact same things, they will likely experience and describe them differently. If we are going to work with girls and with boys in ways that bring out the best in them, then we need to have an understanding of their respective gender cultures—how these cultures determine behavior and influence perspective, what role they play in how girls and boys come to view themselves, the value accorded to each by the larger society in which we live and how that society limits or nurtures the potential of girls and boys. We have to recognize and acknowledge that our strengths as women in working with and relating to girls comes from the gender commonalties that we share with them. Because these characteristics can often make it difficult for us as women to work with boys, we also need to identify and understand those areas of the male culture that make us uncomfortable.

As I describe the female and male gender cultures you might find that some girls and boys (or women and men) that you know don't fit precisely into these categories—such as aggressive girls and nurturing boys. Please keep in mind that I am describing averages and medians, or talking about the polarities of the continuum of human behavior. While as women or men we share characteristics that are common to our sex, as individuals we are all different and exhibit behaviors across the wide continuum of human traits.

Biology–the differences begin in the brain

From conception, girls and boys are programmed to march to different drummers. Fusion between the egg and sperm determines genetic sex—whether they will be a chromosomal XX girl or an XY boy. Steroid or sex hormones called androgens and estrogens act as chemical messengers to ensure that these genetic programs are carried out. For the first six weeks of gestation all fetuses develop along female lines. Then the androgen testosterone separates the boys from the girls by stimulating the development of embryonic male genitalia in XY fetuses. At a certain point in the development of the fetus, it interacts with the nerve cells or neurons that make up the brain and signals for dramatic changes that alter the brain structure into one that is male. In the female fetus the ovaries also produce tiny amounts of testosterone which is required by the developing female brain. Regardless of the sex of the fetus, the more testosterone that bathes the brain at this time, the more that adult will exhibit male behavior. The lesser the amount of testosterone, the more feminine the behavior.

Gender differences between girls and boys are evident shortly after birth. Girls show a tendency to be interested in people and communication, while boys tend to be interested in dynamic activity and in inert objects. Studies of babies 2-4 days old show that girls pay attention longer when adults are speaking and spend almost twice as long maintaining eye contact. While girls lose interest when the connection is broken, boys are equally happy to jabber away at toys and look at abstract geometric designs. The female brain responds more intensely to emotion. Feelings, especially sadness, activate neurons in an area eight times larger in the female brain than in the male. Even before they can understand language, girls seem to be better at identifying the emotional content of speech. As girls grow older they can detect the emotions of others more accurately than boys can. Because the male brain is specially designed for logical problem-solving, it can often take boys up to seven hours longer to process emotional data.

From infancy, girls have a longer attention span than boys who look at objects for shorter but more active periods. Boys take in less sensory information than girls. They smell less, taste less, and get less input and soothing feedback from tactile information. They hear less well, but hear better through one ear than through the other. Because they receive more testosterone and less seratonin—the neurotransmitter that inhibits aggression—boys are more aggressive and impulsive than girls are.

Girls and boys have different perceptions, priorities, behaviors and skills because of differences in their brains and in the ways that they process information. The female brain is 10 to 15% smaller than the male brain but the regions dedicated to higher cognitive functions such as language are more densely packed with neurons. It is more diffuse than the male brain. The functional division between the left and right sides of the brain is less clearly defined so that both sides are used in verbal and visual activities. This means that girls learn to speak earlier than boys do and develop more skill at verbal memory, which helps them master grammar and the intricacies of language at an earlier age.

Male brains are more compartmentalized and therefore more specialized than female ones. The left side is almost exclusively set aside for the control of verbal abilities including speaking, writing, reading and language. The right side controls visual abilities including spatial relations and abstract thoughts. The focused structure of the male brain means that boys can concentrate more intensely than girls can on one thing at a time. They have better hand/eye coordination. They are better able to visualize and manipulate objects in space—which makes them more efficient at interpreting maps, solving mazes and doing the kinds of mathematics that involve abstract concepts of space, relationships and theory. Because their brain does the task and then turns off, boys are more task-oriented than girls.

It is important to remember that neither brain structure is 'superior' to the other. Nor are girls and boys restricted in what they can do because of the structure of their brains. Girls can excel in math and boys can develop a high proficiency in verbal and communication skills. However, because different parts of the male brain grow at different times and at different rates than the corresponding parts of the female brain, girls and boys

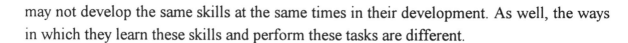

may not develop the same skills at the same times in their development. As well, the ways in which they learn these skills and perform these tasks are different.

Psychology–the effects of development and societal influence

Societal culture and socialization build and expand upon what we bring into the world. Biology and culture form a circle in which one influence feeds the other, making it difficult to pinpoint if something is exclusively biological, cultural or the result of the interplay between them. As a result, theories which attempt to describe the psychological development of girls and boys evolve out of and are influenced by the biological proclivities of each gender and the cultural beliefs of a particular time.

Understanding boys: Popular theories of male development—such as the ones put forth by Freud and Erikson—tend to be congruent with and reflect the values espoused by our society which is also male in perspective. These theories are hierarchical, goal-oriented and individualistic. They see development as occurring in progressive stages, with each stage in turn reinforcing certain qualities that are considered to be more appropriate and mature than those previous. These theories are based upon an assumption that boys develop an identity and sense of self that is based on their individual accomplishments and on how well they perform in the world. In order for them to become independent and able to stand on their own two feet, boys need to separate from their mothers at an early age.

The activities that boys are involved in and the ways that they carry them out serve to reinforce their goal-oriented sense of self and form the basis for their self-esteem. Boys play in large groups, where they can exercise their need for physical activity and for controlling more territory. They are a lot more physical with one another than girls are. Team sports teach boys about rules, about winning and losing, about being the best—being on top. Competition offers boys a way in which to feel worthy. Boys are better able to tolerate conflict than girls are. Conflict often becomes the basis for their friendships and their games and is often a way for them to relate to one another, check each other out and take a first step towards friendship. Loyalty plays a big part in their friendships as boys learn to bond with each other in 'us-against-them' scenarios. Interpersonal communication is often most comfortable when it takes place in the context of an activity—when boys interact and work side by side rather than face to face.

Boys assess each situation in terms of how adequately they perform in relation to one another. Their comfort level comes from knowing where they fit in and what they must do to improve or maintain their status. Possession of information allows boys to gain power over someone else. Male language, which is based upon logical reasoning, serves as a way for boys to capture and hold onto another person's attention and to put forth their opinions and views in such a way that they 'win' the discussion (or at least hold their own).

Recent research on boys shows that our society encourages boys to separate from their mothers prematurely. This creates an impasse in their emotional development as boys shut down their feelings in order to become self-reliant. Because relatively few fathers are involved in the immediate care of their children, most boys grow up having no one with whom to develop lasting emotional connections. Since intimacy is not addressed in this developmental scheme until boys reach adolescence, it is often intertwined and confused with sexuality.

Understanding girls: Psychologists Jean Baker Miller, Janet Surrey and other researchers at the Stone Center at Wellesley College, and Carol Gilligan and her colleagues at Harvard University have studied female development for more than twenty years. Their theories of female psychology demonstrate the divergent paths that girls and boys follow as they grow up.

Girls grow up with a perception of the world that is less individualistic and more contextual than that of boys. Because they are not encouraged to separate from their mothers at an early age, girls develop a core structure (or 'self-in-relation') which evolves out of this early relationship. Their identity is based on their experience of themselves in relationships. These relationships involve mutual understanding, emotional support and the commitment of both individuals to the development of each person and to the relationship itself. Girls grow up to be interdependent. They learn to evaluate situations not only in terms of their individual responses, but also within the context of whatever 'others' may be involved. It is because the world of relationships makes up so much of female experience that girls grow up concerned not only with their own individual well-being, but also with the well-being of all those systems in which they participate.

The relational and contextual perspective that girls develop forms the basis of their female gender culture. It influences how they learn, the stories that they tell (and the ways in which they tell them), what they think is important and how they get things done. Girls play in small groups that are based on communication and connection. Their games teach them empathy and sensitivity and have fewer rules than those of boys. Girls will change the rules to accommodate situations that arise. While competition can be a part of their games, they tend to place more emphasis on inclusion and on taking turns. Girls handle conflict differently than boys. They will try to compromise and negotiate with one another. If there is no resolution, they will find indirect ways of showing disapproval. For example, threatening to exclude the other person is generally more effective (and more hurtful) than using physical force.

When girls interact with one another they feel nourished by their common experiences, common language and relational bonds. Relationships play a major part in their sense of well being. Girls have a best friend. They tell each other secrets. Their friendships are based on intimacy, connection and sharing. Girls use language and communication as a way of drawing people closer to them. The exchange of similar experiences ensures that girls are equal in vulnerability and therefore in power. Attempting to offer advice before establishing equality places the person giving the advice on top, and impairs the balance of the relationship.

Because girls are interdependent they travel in pairs. Whenever they need to solve problems and make decisions they talk to a friend. If the problem or decision is a big one, they talk to two friends (or more). Talking allows them to try out different solutions and to ask for and receive feedback before they make up their mind. When girls enter new situations they assess how close or how distant they are from the other person. Their sense of security depends on feeling connected. When girls experience distance, they become anxious and often blame themselves for the failure to connect. Girls work best together through a process that involves verbally sharing things about themselves to establish intimacy and connection, then working to discover a commonality in order to develop equality, then finally addressing the task at hand.

When gender cultures clash

When girls and boys move out of their respective cultures they experience the difficulties of trying to relate to others who have a totally different perception of and orientation to the world than they do. When I first met my husband, our telephone conversations were fraught with gender misunderstandings. Dan would call and ask about my day. I would give him a blow by blow account of every interaction I had and everything that I did. As I showered him with details I would become aware of silence at the other end of the phone. 'Are you listening?' I would ask, beginning to feel anxious. 'Yes, yes, go on,' he would respond. And so I would continue until once again I would feel that the phone had 'died.' *This man really doesn't care about me*, I would think as I checked one more time to see if he was still there. 'Yes, yes, go on,' he would respond, frustration evident in his voice. I eventually came to understand this dynamic as a *gender difference*.

When we as women talk to one another, we continuously interject with empathic exclamations such as 'uh huh,' 'cool,' 'that's awful.' We interrupt each other frequently in order to make sure that we understand one another. We share similar experiences of our own. Our conversations never follow a straight line but meander through the process of our interaction. When I talked to Dan, I expected him to respond in the same way. When he didn't, I misinterpreted his silence as disinterest and therefore as his desire to create distance between us. I didn't know that conversation had a totally different function for him. Men enter into conversations not to create intimacy but to try to define the problem so that they can fix it. Dan was silent because he was patiently waiting for me to get to the point. When I didn't do that, he became more and more frustrated. How was he going to let me know that he cared for me if he couldn't tell me what to do? Once we were able to recognize the gender differences, we could deepen the relationship between us.

If only we could become *bi-cultural* we could more easily learn from one another and bridge the gap between women and men. We could move freely back and forth along the whole continuum of human behavior and open up a wide range of different behaviors and options for all of us. We could structure activities and institutions so that they served the needs of both cultures, not just one.

The continuum of human behavior is lopsided because not all gender characteristics are considered equal in all situations. When girls and boys attempt to enter into areas that are governed by a gender culture that is not theirs and which attempts to impose this other view upon them, they reach an impasse or crisis in their development which profoundly affects their sense of self. The chapter on boys will address what happens to them—especially when they enter the female world of the elementary school system. The next chapter will describe what happens to girls at adolescence when they seek to enter the larger world, which is predominantly male.

Sources:

Deborah Blum. *Sex on the Brain: The Biological Differences Between Men and Women.* New York: Viking, 1997.

Erik Erikson. *Identity, Youth and Crisis.* New York: W. W. Norton, 1968.

Carol Gilligan and Lynn Mikel Brown. *Meeting at the Crossroads: Women's Psychology and Girls' Development.* Cambridge: Harvard University Press, 1992.

Anne Moir and David Jessel. *Brain Sex: The Real Difference between Men and Women.* New York: Bantam Doubleday Dell, 1991.

Amy Sheldon. "Pickle Fights: Gendered Talk in Preschool Disputes," in Deborah Tannen, ed. *Gender and Conversational Interaction.* New York: Oxford University Press, 1993.

Janet L. Surrey. "The Self-in-Relation: A Theory of Women's Development," in Judith Jordan, Alexandra G. Kaplan, Jean Baker Miller, Irene P. Stiver & Janet L. Surrey, eds. *Women's Growth in Connection: Writings from the Stone Center.* New York: Guilford Press, 1991.

Deborah Tannen. *You Just Don't Understand: Women and Men in Conversation.* New York: Ballantine Books, 1990.

FEMALE ADOLESCENCE

Adolescence is the period of time between childhood and adulthood. Early adolescence takes place between the ages of 11 to 13, middle adolescence between 14 to 16, and late adolescence between 17 to 20. Adolescence is a crucial time in female development. Girls experience profound biological, cultural, social, emotional and behavioral changes in their lives. They suffer more than boys do from depression, concerns about appearance, fear for personal safety, social and emotional stress, and other signs of psychological distress. Many girls lose their sense of self as well as their self-confidence and self-worth. In order for us to understand why this happens we need to understand the tremendous power of traditional socialization and the influence it has on girls as they make the transition from childhood though adolescence and into adulthood.

In the early years of elementary school, most girls feel good about themselves and about their abilities. They mature faster than boys, develop better control of the small motor skills which enable them to write and draw, develop math and reading skills earlier, and have good social skills which help them get along with others. Girls flower in this environment, because it is congruent with their stage of development and because it emphasizes cooperation, communication and learning in small groups. At eight years of age, girls are as tall as boys are and, because they weigh more on the average, they are physically stronger. Because they are still relatively free from the full impact of socialization, they have access to and express the whole range of their feelings. Their behavior is relatively unrestricted. Until the age of 10, girls are psychologically healthier and have fewer behavioral problems than boys.

As girls reach adolescence they experience conflicts and obstacles in the basic healthy expression of their need for connection with others—connections which form the basis of their identity. Because the adult world stresses self-sufficiency, autonomy, assertiveness and competition, the relational qualities, characteristics and skills that give them their sense of self and self-worth are devalued and seen as deficient. Seen through this male perspective, their self-expression is labeled over-reaction and/or hysteria. Their interdependence is interpreted as dependency and neediness—evidence that girls constantly need approval and have trouble making up their minds. Because men who exhibit these same characteristics in public are discounted as weaklings and are viewed as wimps, girls are led to discount and negate these positive qualities in themselves.

The changes that girls make in their relationships

Carol Gilligan and her colleagues have been studying the psychological development of girls over time. They found that during adolescence girls experience profound changes in the way that they negotiate their friendships and relationships that impact greatly on their identity and sense of self. As girls approach adolescence, they begin to struggle with the loss of their voice (that is, their ability to speak out and to voice their opinions) as well as their ability to take their own experiences seriously. Gilligan points out a fundamental paradox that develops in girls' (and then women's) lives: though the desire for connection and mutually responsive relationships make up an integral part of female identity, adolescent girls and adult women learn to silence themselves in relationships and negate their own selves rather than risk open conflict that might lead to rejection, isolation and even violence against themselves.

As girls grow up they are bombarded with messages from the culture (including messages from grown women such as ourselves) that it is better to be kind and nice and not hurt anyone's feelings than to be honest and say what they really think and feel. Girls are faced with a psychological dilemma: if they say what they are feeling and thinking they are in danger of losing their relationships—but if they don't speak their minds and their hearts, they lose the authenticity of their relationships and therefore their connection with others. In the process, they lose themselves. Because the 'popular' girl is the one who is nice and fits in, girls' censor themselves. They say to themselves: 'I shouldn't say that' or 'They don't agree with me so I'll just keep my mouth shut.'

The *tyranny of kind and nice* causes girls to cover their strong feelings, hold back their opinions and hide their own truths from themselves. In the process they split into two selves—the real inner self and the false, pleasing persona. As the real self becomes buried and the false one takes its place, girls move from being the center of their own experiences to looking outward for definition. The more that they please other people the more they lose their inner voice, their awareness of their own needs and their ability to form and trust their own perceptions. As a result they dissociate from their experiences, their feelings and their true selves.

The adaptations which girls make in their behavior

During adolescence girls make major adaptations in their behavior in order to be included in the male world. Imagine that you are having coffee with a small group of women. They could be your friends or they could be colleagues at work. You're talking about a book that you read, a movie that you saw, or a situation where you were required to take charge. During the discussion you exchange ideas and share your opinions freely and sometimes passionately. Then a man joins the group. The conversation becomes less spontaneous and the focus shifts as he takes over its direction and sets a different tone for the discussion. Instead of his having to accommodate his language and way of communicating to your female style, all of you accommodate yourselves to his.

Imagine that later on, you are asked to describe the same book, movie, and/or situation to a larger group (in a meeting, perhaps). As you think of how you might phrase things for this kind of an audience, you attempt to translate your ideas from a female-oriented language/style into the predominant one that is male and goal-oriented. As you do so, you begin to lose your nuances, context and frame of reference. You become unsure of your ground and begin to doubt the validity of what you have to say. Your voice becomes more hesitant as you qualify your opinions with phrases such as 'This is not important, but...' 'This is probably wrong, but...' You soon begin to wonder if your opinions are at all important and to question whether, indeed, you have anything at all worth saying. Because you are afraid of being laughed at or being wrong, you stop speaking out in larger groups—especially mixed gender groups.

The changes that girls experience in their bodies

At the same time that girls are experiencing changes in their behavior, their bodies change. Their hips get bigger during puberty and they accumulate the fat necessary for them to become sexual women. The discrepancy between the narrowly defined cultural ideal and their genetic and biological heritage begins to widen. Girls come to believe that the changes in their bodies are not normal and that their bodies are unacceptable or deformed. Because the ideal weight is lower than what is normal or healthy, girls who do not conform to this ideal biologically begin a life-long struggle against the needs of their bodies to be comfortable at a higher weight. Their self-esteem becomes bound up with weight-control rather than with self-expression. Many girls associate the inevitable weight gain and increase in body fat that occurs during puberty with the societal restrictions that are imposed on them. Because they have no language or awareness with which to deal with the restrictions in their lives they deflect their feelings of distress and powerlessness onto the changes in their bodies. They focus on their reflected external image instead of on their real internal selves. They feel fat.

How girls deal with distress

Most girls are socialized to repress their feelings and internalize their distress—to draw their pain into themselves. Instead of addressing situations directly, they blame themselves. They ask 'What's wrong with me? What did I do?' They talk about being angry with themselves. They tend to be overly concerned about what people think about them, and often seek to please others at the expense of themselves. When girls internalize their distress they often experience physical symptoms such as headaches and

10.

stomachaches. They also become vulnerable to depression, thoughts of suicide and to the preoccupation with food and weight that can lead to disordered eating and to eating disorders.

Some girls externalize or act out their distress. They transform their feelings into anger and blame, which they direct against whoever or whatever they feel has triggered the feelings. These girls are more likely to have a higher use of drugs and alcohol, and to engage in violence against other girls. Some girls externalize their distress through sexual activity and often become pregnant. A study of fourth grade girls who were getting into trouble with teachers and breaking rules, but maintained their popularity with their peers, found that 40% had a child by the time that they finished high school.

Speaking the language of fat

As girls grow up and are prohibited from expressing their feelings directly, they learn to do so indirectly through the use of a negative voice. Girls tell themselves that they 'feel stupid' and that they 'feel ugly.' Because girls are socialized to value themselves according to how they look and because fat is considered bad by our society, many girls 'feel fat.' They deflect the feelings that they cannot express onto their bodies and encode them in a *language of fat*.

When girls speak of 'feeling fat' they are not referring to their size. Thin girls feel fat and fat girls feel fat. Nobody feels fat all the time. If at two o'clock, for example, someone felt fine and at two-thirty she felt fat, the change that took place was not physical. It was emotional. Instead of dealing with situations directly, girls learn to speak in code. They feel fat when they are angry, sad, lonely, and insecure, when they have no language for their emotions or feel unsafe in expressing them. Speaking in code causes girls to shift their focus from the internal sense-of-self at the center of their experiences to their external image. Without a sense of their own true selves to guide them, girls look outward for definition and rely on other people's opinions—which reinforce the alienation from their selves and the detachment from their bodies that they are already beginning to feel.

The major risks to girls

The Psychologically Healthy Girl
✓ Is able to be clear about what she wants.
✓ Has a wide range of feelings, which include anger, and can express them constructively.
✓ Makes healthy choices rather than reacts to situations.
✓ Has a good sense of boundaries—is able to say yes and no.
✓ Has developed her self-esteem in areas other than just looking good.
✓ Have connections with others that are based on mutuality and honest engagement.

Until adolescence, girls flourish if they are allowed and encouraged to be truthful about their feelings and opinions if the people in their lives engage with them honestly, if they have not experienced major family problems/disruptions, and if they have not been sexually or physically abused or witnessed violence first-hand.

During adolescence girls experience changes in every aspect of their individual development, as well as in every major social context. Changes in their bodies during puberty affect their body image. The move from the intimacy of the small elementary school to the larger and more impersonal junior high or high school disrupts their peer groups and often causes the loss of friendships. Girls experience profound changes in the ways they negotiate their relationships. Their sense of self erodes as their connections with others become frayed and distorted. Girls may also experience stressful life events during adolescence such as ongoing conflict with parents, the divorce of their parents, sexual harassment and abusive relationships with boys.

The major risks to girls during adolescence are eating disorders and depression (with its accompanying risk of suicide). Although we don't need to be experts in these areas, we do need to understand their dynamics. We need to know the warning signs so that we can recognize when girls are experiencing difficulty and assist them in obtaining the appropriate help. Addressing eating disorders and depression also provides a framework for addressing other issues that have their roots in the same experience of growing up female in a male world. These include smoking, sexually transmitted diseases, teen pregnancy, alcohol and drug use, and abusive relationships.

DISORDERED EATING AND EATING DISORDERS

*Warning Signs...*someone at risk or coping with an eating disorder may be:
- ✓ Obsessed with their appearance
- ✓ Constantly `feeling fat' and making comments about their weight
- ✓ Weighing themselves at least once a day
- ✓ Avoiding eating with others
- ✓ Putting themselves down and being overly sensitive to criticism
- ✓ Frequently depressed or irritable
- ✓ Fasting, bingeing and/or exercising excessively
- ✓ Needing to be perfect in everything they do
- ✓ Withdrawing from their friends or family
- ✓ Experiencing loss or disruption of friendships

While many girls feel fat not all girls will develop an eating disorder. Anorexia and bulimia are part of a continuum of disordered eating that includes compulsive eating, chronic 'normalized' dieting, weight preoccupation, and body dissatisfaction (*see* Handout H-1). An eating disorder exists when the preoccupation with food and weight becomes an *obsession*, when the behaviors around food are driven primarily by psychological need, when everything becomes valued according to the numbers on the bathroom scale.

While eating disorders are expressions of food/weight issues, they are not merely problems with food or with weight. Girls use the preoccupation with food and weight to deal with feelings that are very painful or are considered inappropriate to express—such as anger, sexuality, insecurity, loneliness and need. They use it to deal with tension and anxiety, with emotional conflict, and with difficulties that they cannot resolve. Girls use disordered eating and eating disorder behaviors as a means of dealing with their transition into an adult world that devalues the relational structure of the female culture. They externalize those feelings and characteristics that are judged unacceptable to them or to society. Because the perfect girl is thin, unemotional, competent, and always self-confident and in control, girls dissociate from those parts of themselves that they hesitate to acknowledge and redirect these real life concerns into their fear of being fat.

Eating disorders occur at various developmental stages. Before puberty incidents of anorexia nervosa are almost equal for girls and boys. During adolescence they increase dramatically in girls in response to the changes in their bodies and their lives. Bulimia nervosa, which usually does not occur before adolescence, is also predominant in girls.

There are many reasons why girls develop eating disorders. Girls who mature early weigh more than their peers. Early dieting behavior changes their metabolism so that they have to engage in more and more risk-taking activities in order to lose weight. Girls who have a tendency toward perfectionism, who have low self-esteem, who have a sense of ineffectiveness in their lives, who lack intimate connections in their lives and/or who have experienced changes or loss in their major relationships are often at greater risk. So are girls who have been sexually or physically abused, experienced a recent divorce in the family, or whose parents are chronically depressed or abuse alcohol or drugs. Ineffective communication in families, rigid boundaries that don't allow girls room to grow, or a lack of boundaries which make them unsafe are also contributing factors. Girls who are teased about their weight are also at risk, as well as those who live in a culture of dieting—where their mothers and friends diet and where they read teen magazines that reinforce a 'thin' image.

The greatest risk factor for girls is internalizing the values and behaviors of the male culture and in the process rejecting their own. Psychologist Catherine Steiner-Adair explored the conflicts between the relational aspects of female identity and the societal image of independence, achievement and autonomy in a study of 32 girls ages 14 through 18 attending Emma Willard School in Troy, New York. Two distinct patterns emerged. 'Wise women' recognized societal pressure for achievement and independence, but retained values focused on the importance of relationships. 'Superwomen' identified with an ideal woman who was successful in many different roles so that she could gain external approval. The 'superwomen' saw the ideal woman as independent and therefore not needing anyone and as being tall and thin.

Steiner-Adair concluded that girls who are able to identify cultural values such as autonomy; independence and success for women but are still able to maintain their own sometimes conflicting values are at less risk for eating disorders. Those girls who most strongly identify with societal values that are in conflict with their developmental needs for connection are at greater risk.

DEPRESSION

*Warning Signs...*someone at risk for depression may show:

- ✓ Declining school performance
- ✓ Persistent expression of helpless or hopeless attitude
- ✓ Gloomy moods that persist for two weeks without improvement
- ✓ Sudden lack of interest in activities outside school
- ✓ Recent loss of a loved one, especially a family member
- ✓ Abrupt changes in behavior, including hyperactivity and/or withdrawal from family and friends
- ✓ Changes in sleeping and/or eating habits
- ✓ Family problems such as parents' divorce or traumatic change
- ✓ Evidence that she is being put down, rejected, alienated
- ✓ Absence of normal social contacts
- ✓ Impulsiveness and erratic behavior not true to form
- ✓ Giving away cherished possessions
- ✓ Thoughts of suicide, self-hatred, self-destruction

Although depression is occasionally found in childhood, it more often develops and increases dramatically in adolescence. Depression exists on a continuum. Everyone feels sad, blue and unhappy from time to time. Low in energy, tired, unable to concentrate and/or worried. One can feel bleak and not care about anything. One can feel anxious, eat too much or too little, sleep too much or not enough, cry a lot and withdraw from friends. But for most people these feelings soon fade. Clinical depression may resemble these emotional dips but it is much more pervasive, long lasting, and life threatening.

Clinical depression is defined as a cluster of identifiable symptoms where at least five things happen together for at least two weeks duration. The person must experience either a depressed or irritable mood and/or a loss of interest in most things—as well as however many of the following make up the total of five symptoms: insomnia or oversleeping, loss of appetite, overeating or weight gain, fatigue or loss of energy, physical or mental agitation or slowing down, lack of concentration or decisiveness, feelings of worthlessness or guilt, and recurring thoughts of death or suicide. Preadolescent/adolescent onset of clinical depression is considered to be a serious risk factor for adult depression and other major psychiatric disorders.

It is important to note that two individuals with depression may look and feel different from each other. One person may be very tired, sleep and eat a lot, and slow down her activities. The other may be agitated, pace around, and not eat and sleep very much. Adolescents who experience depression may have other emotional disorders. For boys this can be disruptive behavior such as acting out, while girls are more likely to have eating disorders. Whether depression causes these problems or whether these other disorders cause depression is not clear, but as the severity of the depression increases, the intensity of the other disorders increases as well. While most adolescents with depression may have suicidal thoughts, girls attempt suicide more than boys do—but boys succeed more often than girls do.

Before adolescence, boys are somewhat more likely to exhibit depressive symptoms than girls are. Statistics seem to indicate that this reverses significantly after puberty. By the ages of 14-16, girls are twice as likely to be depressed and seem to experience a higher lifetime prevalence of depression than males. However, when looking at these statistics, we need to question whether the differences occur because girls are in fact more depressed or whether instead because depression in girls might be more identifiable. Girls are more willing to talk about their problems and seek help. Boys are socialized to mask their sadness and vulnerability and may fail to admit or even understand that they are depressed.

Depression during adolescence is most likely the result of interacting environmental conditions and individual predisposition rather than one single outstanding factor. Certain kinds of stress may trigger depression—such as learning problems, emotional or sexual or physical abuse, and family problems that have gone on for a long time. So can moving often and changing schools, being sick a lot, divorce in the family, death of a cherished relative or friend, or rejection by a close friend. Having a depressed parent is a major risk for depression. So is the use of alcohol or drugs. Depression can also occur because of a viral illness, or an imbalance in the thyroid or other key parts of the hormonal system. It can also result from taking certain prescription drugs.

Many girls and boys become depressed because they are socialized to repress certain feelings. During puberty, girls are socialized to close down all feelings except for those that have to do with vulnerability and relationships. Boys are only entitled to express anger and rage. Depressing one's feelings requires a great deal of emotional energy. You might want to try the following experiment in order to understand how depression works: Sit down in a comfortable chair. Extend your arms with your hands palm up. Make fists of your hands. Holding your fists closed as tightly as you can slowly bring your fists towards your body. The amount of tension in your arms and shoulders is a good indication of how much energy it takes to hold your feelings inside.

Sources:

Kenneth Dodge, "Emotion and Social Information Processing," in J. Garber and K. Dodge, *The Development of Emotion Regulation and Dysregulation*. New York: Cambridge University Press, 1991.

Sandra Susan Friedman. *When Girls Feel Fat: Helping Girls Through Adolescence*. Toronto: HarperCollins, 1997.

E. Jane Garland. *Depression is the Pits, But I'm Getting Better: A Guide for Adolescents*. Washington, DC: Magination Press, 1997.

Czesia Fuks Geddes. "Adolescent Depression: Recognition and Help-Seeking in a Population Based Sample," MSW Thesis, University of Melbourne, March 1997 (unpublished).

Carol Gilligan and Lynn Mikel Brown. *Meeting at the Crossroads: Women's Psychology and Girls' Development*. Cambridge: Harvard University Press, 1992.

D. Offord, M.H. Boyle, P. Szatmari et al. "Ontario Child and Health Study II: Six Month Prevalence of Disorder and rates of Service Utilization." *Arch. Gen. Psych.* 1987, vol. 44.

Anne C. Petersen, Bruce E. Compas, Jeanne Brooks-Gunn, Mark Stemmler, Sydney Ey and Kathleen E. Grant. "Depression in Adolescence," *American Psychologist,* 1993, 48(2): 155-168.

Linda Smolak and Michael P. Levine. "Adolescent Transitions and the Development of Eating Problems," in Linda Smolak, Michael P. Levine and Ruth Striegel-Moore. *The Developmental Psychopathology of Eating Disorders: Implications for Research, Prevention and Treatment*. New Jersey: Lawrence Erlbaum Associates, 1996.

Laurence Steinberg. *Adolescence* (second edition). New York: Alfred A. Knopf, Inc., 1989, p. 417-422.

Catherine Steiner-Adair, "The Body Politic: Normal Female Adolescent Development and the Development of Eating Disorders," *Journal of the American Academy of Psychoanalysis,* 55, 567-576, 1986.

CORE

THE *JUST FOR GIRLS* PROGRAM

JUST FOR GIRLS is a group program that addresses the silencing of girls' voices in adolescence and the subsequent social and health risks that this causes. It is based upon a belief that disordered eating, eating disorders, depression and other such risks are coping mechanisms developed in order to deal with the stressors in girls' lives. These include personal stressors and, in particular, the societal stressor of growing up female in a male world that discounts and distorts the relational nature of girls' gender culture. Because 'feeling fat' is an almost universal concern among girls, teaching them how to decode their own *language of fat* encourages self-expression, provides a key to opening discussion about what happens to them as they grow up, and provides them with skills so that they can retain their voice and remain true to themselves as they develop into women.

GOALS OF THE PROGRAM

1. To help girls become aware of and decode the *language of fat* before it becomes entrenched as a means of self-expression and internalized as a way for them to cope with difficult feelings and situations in their lives.

2. To help girls develop and maintain their sense of self by encouraging their self-expression and validating their experiences. This includes providing them with an understanding of their behavior, feelings and experiences that is framed in the context of their socialization in the female gender culture.

3. To help girls build support systems for themselves by encouraging and facilitating the connections that they have with each other and with adult women.

17.

CORE STRUCTURE OF THE GROUP

The group operates according to the *core structure* outlined here, which is repeated each week. I will elaborate on the various components as they appear in the chapter:

» Each session is one and one half-hours long. If the group is too short, it is hard to develop good group dynamics or to ensure that each girl feels heard. If the group is too long, we lose their attention.

» The facilitator begins her group by sharing a little of who she is. She describes the purpose of the group and lets the girls know what is expected of them. She assures the girls that there is no right or wrong—nobody can *fail* the group.

» The girls are reassured that they have complete confidentiality unless they are in situations where they are in danger (by law, sexual abuse must be reported to the appropriate authorities). This means that what they say will not be repeated to their parents or their teachers without their permission, that no one will talk about them when they leave the room, and that they themselves will not talk about what people reveal once they are outside of the group.

» Each week the girls are asked to remember a time the previous week when they were 'hit by a *grungie*.' That is, when they felt or told themselves that they were fat, ugly, stupid, etc. They are asked to talk about what else was happening at that particular time. They are encouraged to tell the story again—but this time without the *grungie*, to express the real feelings that are part of the story. The facilitator validates their experiences and feelings and provides them with a context that is framed in female culture and socialization.

» The custom of the Talking Stick has been borrowed from the First Nations people. As the Talking Stick is passed around the group, only the person holding it may speak. The Talking Stick is used to ensure that each girl has an opportunity to speak uninterrupted and to be listened to, and this provides each girl with an opportunity to develop her own voice.

» Activities are included and topics are introduced that address the developmental issues of the age group involved. They encourage self-expression, address girls' concerns, build communication skills and help girls accept their natural bodies.

» Taking a break during the session is optional. So is providing food and/or juice.

» At the close of each session, each girl is encouraged to say something positive about herself, about her abilities, or about what makes her interesting as a person.

SETTING UP THE PROGRAM

Location

The first groups that I facilitated were held in community centers in order to give girls who have difficulties at home or in school (or both) a place where they can perceive themselves in a positive light. Holding the group outside of the school makes an easier transition from the school setting to the informality of the group. In the school setting girls have to raise their hands to speak and they are always conscious of being wrong and being disciplined. The neutral environment means that the facilitators are less likely to be seen as authority figures, which makes it easier for girls to try out different behaviors. The difficulty in holding the group outside the school is in finding a nearby location that it is easily available to girls whose mothers do not have access to a car or are unavailable to drive them after school.

While holding the group in the school has its drawbacks, it is the most convenient and logical place because that is where the girls are located. It is important to find a place that is safe, to make sure that the group is not described as one for girls with 'problems' and to ensure privacy and confidentiality. When teachers facilitate or co-facilitate these groups they need to be comfortable making the change from the formality of the classroom to the intimacy of the group. They also need to be able to create boundaries with the girls so that what goes on in the group does not infiltrate the classroom and vice versa.

While groups are often held after school, holding groups during the school day as part of the school program ensures better attendance and reaches girls who might need this the most. While girls in grades five, six and seven will participate in the group whenever it is held, girls in grade eight and nine are reluctant to participate if the group is held after school. Many just want to hang out with their friends or boyfriends. Some girls have other commitments such as sports, jobs and taking care of younger siblings.

Group format

JUST FOR GIRLS is held over a ten to twelve week period. This gives the girls time to build up trust, and to learn and practice new skills. You can hold your group on a drop-in basis or have the girls register before the group begins. Both have certain advantages. The drop-in format allows girls to try out the activity without making a long-term commitment. It lets them miss sessions because of other demands on their time without feeling guilty. It makes it easier for them to bring friends who might have initially been reluctant to attend.

The first time that I co-facilitated a drop-in group we were afraid that we would be dealing with a totally different group of girls each week, that we would have to turn girls away if a large number showed up and that we would never be able to establish continuity.

That did not happen. The group seemed to maintain a stable attendance. Even though most of the girls who came once usually came back again, girls often had to miss sessions. This allowed new girls to take the places of the girls who were away without increasing the group size too much.

Many facilitators prefer to have girls register ahead of time. Introducing new people into a group once it has begun can affect the group dynamics. Pre-registration allows facilitators to invite selected girls who they consider might be of high risk and more in need of the group than other girls. Some facilities such as community centers require pre-registration in order to determine if there are enough girls for the group to go ahead. Once the group has become well known and popular, pre-registration is often necessary in order to make sure that any one group is not too big in size and that nobody is turned away from the first session.

Group size

The ideal group number is between six and eight participants because that size of group is where girls feel safest. Some groups can function well with ten or even twelve girls as long as you are working with a co-facilitator and can continuously break into smaller groups. In one group that I co-facilitated, we suffered from an embarrassment of riches. The first few weeks we had 6 or 7 grade six girls. Because we were afraid that someday no one would show up, we didn't restrict the group to one grade and continued to invite more girls. Soon grade seven girls began to attend. While we were excited by the interest shown in the group, its mechanics began to fall apart.

At the point where we had 15 girls in attendance the dynamics changed. The girls clammed up. Instead of sharing, they giggled and poked one another. Because girls find it too intimidating to speak in a large group, they divided themselves into smaller groups and spoke only to their friends—and they all spoke at once. The grade 6 girls felt threatened by the grade 7 girls. The grade 7 girls looked down on those in grade 6. After two weeks of tearing our hair out, we split into two groups according to grade.

Deciding who attends

Because all girls are at risk for eating disorders and depression, any girl who fits the age or grade for which the group is targeted is eligible to attend. Sometimes groups are made up of girls considered by their teachers and guidance counselors to be at high risk for eating disorders or depression. These groups can be difficult to facilitate because the girls tend to be similar in personality. It is hard to stimulate group interaction and discussion when most of the girls are introverted and shy. Sometimes teachers and guidance counselors refer girls to the group who are experiencing problems in their lives and have difficulty fitting into the classroom structure. Care must be taken that the focus of the group is on the issues that the girls raise rather than on the symptoms or behaviors that they present. Too often we tend to relate to the anorexia, depression or acting out behaviors and forget about the girls themselves.

JUST FOR GIRLS was developed for facilitators of different orientations, skills, interests and degrees of experience. Not all groups are the same nor are the facilitators who run them. It is important that you evaluate each group that you are about to facilitate in terms of your own skills, your experience, your comfort level and the mandate of the program as a whole. As women, we often think that we should be able to work with every situation and every personality type. Instead of recognizing and setting our limits, we tend to blame ourselves for not being able to deal with situations that are just too difficult or inappropriate for us to handle.

Establishing a protocol for reporting danger or abuse

Before you begin the program it is important that you talk with the agency or school or community center sponsoring the group about the protocols for reporting physical and sexual abuse and any danger that you think a girl might be in. You need to know the laws in your area. In British Columbia, for example, any person who has knowledge of a child who has been or is being physically harmed, sexually abused, sexually exploited or is in danger must report it to the Ministry for Children and Families. This includes girls whose low body weight is not being addressed and who therefore might be at medical risk. You also need to establish protocols for dealing with concerns about suicide, and for addressing the issue of sexual harassment of girls by teachers or other staff members. If you suspect but are unsure that a girl is at risk, or if you are uncomfortable with what a particular girl is saying, contact the appropriate source for advice. Don't be afraid of over-reacting. It's better to be safe than sorry.

To snack or not to snack

One grade seven group that I facilitated was held in the premises of a non-profit organization near several elementary schools. The girls came to the group each week via the grocery store on the corner, laden with enough junk food to support the economy of a small sugar-producing country. We never made an issue of their choices because many adolescent girls use junk food as a way of asserting their independence. Above all we wanted them to come to the group. The next time that we held a group at this facility, we let the girls know ahead of time that we would provide the snacks.

When groups are held after school it is a good idea to provide snacks. Adolescent girls are hungry because they are growing, many of them have an erratic relationship with food

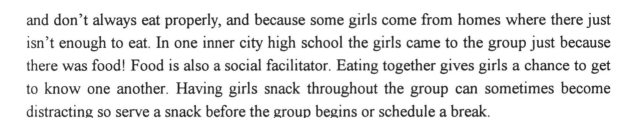

and don't always eat properly, and because some girls come from homes where there just isn't enough to eat. In one inner city high school the girls came to the group just because there was food! Food is also a social facilitator. Eating together gives girls a chance to get to know one another. Having girls snack throughout the group can sometimes become distracting so serve a snack before the group begins or schedule a break.

Inviting girls to the group

Because so many girls are afraid of doing the wrong thing, they need to know what the group is about and what is expected of them before they will take the risk of trying it out. The best way to ensure attendance is to go into the schools involved and speak just to the girls in the targeted grade. This allows them to form a connection with you and makes it safer for them to attend the first time. I learned very quickly that if the classes were mixed by gender, the girls were inhibited by the boys and remained silent. If they were mixed by grade, the younger girls were intimidated by the power imbalance. Handout H-2 will help you put together your presentation. Tailor it to fit your own needs and style.

Sometimes it is not possible to speak to the girls before the group begins. In that case, notices and advertisements should emphasize the group as a time 'just for girls'—where they can learn about other girls' experiences with the issues that also affect them and talk about the things that concern them. Topics such as boys, friends, teasing, families and school should be mentioned because girls are more likely to participate in programs that address issues that are of immediate concern to them. Although eating disorders, depression, body image and self-esteem are issues that girls deal with, the group should not be defined in those terms because girls don't like to be seen as having a problem. As well, limiting the description to these particular issues leads girls to believe that there won't be any opportunity to talk about anything else.

Informing parents

It is important to let parents know what the group is about and what topics will be covered. Handout H-3 shows a sample flyer that you can adapt and give to the girls when you first invite them to the group. The flyer also contains a consent form that the girls should return to you. Parental support is important because parents can reinforce the skills that are taught in the group—such as recognizing and articulating the *grungies*. In one group for grade ten girls the facilitators planned a pizza night and invited the girls to bring their mothers. They ran a mini-session so that the mothers could learn about the *grungies* and they talked about some of the issues that were of concern to the girls. This opened up the lines of communication between mothers and daughters. However, when the same facilitators attempted to hold an information meeting for the parents of grade eight girls, very few mothers attended. Often parents want to be involved but can't be, because they are juggling so many different commitments.

While most parents support the *JUST FOR GIRLS* program, some don't. When the groups require preregistration or classes require consent, parents can prevent their daughters from participating. In groups where no consent form is required or when the group is integrated into the school curriculum, girls often attend even though their parents may not know or may be against it. When a participant in one grade eight group cried during a session, she became concerned that her eyes were red. 'My parents don't want me to come to the group,' she said. 'They think it's a waste of time. I tell them that on Tuesdays I play volleyball.'

Even when parents consent to their daughters' participation, they sometimes don't realize that addressing girls' issues and concerns will involve changes in their behavior. In one group a father complained because his daughter was speaking her mind more. 'She used to be such a good girl, She would do everything that I told her to. Now she disagrees with me and it's all because of that group.'

Girls who attend the group despite their parents' wishes have to deal with the conflict between the values taught at home and the skills and philosophy taught in the group. This is especially true of girls who come from cultures where women are seen as inferior to men and where their voices are not supposed to be heard. When girls continue to attend the group even with opposition at home, the group can encourage them to practice their communication skills and to use their voice in situations that are less threatening to them than outright confrontation with their parents. It can also validate the girls' feelings of being caught between needing to be themselves and being pressured to conform to their families' ideals.

PLANNING YOUR SESSIONS

The core structure of each session can be divided into four parts: the *Opening* where an atmosphere of safety is created; the *Grungie Circle* which is the key component of the program; a specific *Topic* with activities and discussion that encourage self-expression; and the *Closing* which is a time to build self esteem.

In the SESSION PLANS section I have provided sample session or lesson plans to help you get started. There are far more session plans than there will be weeks of the group. Each session plan is full of activities. You do not have to do all of them in the same session. You can adapt those plans that you feel comfortable with to your own needs and the needs of your particular group. You can combine them, substitute activities that I have suggested, and you can use the plans in whatever order you see fit. You can even ignore them if you wish. Please keep in mind that all groups are different and that as you gain more experience you will probably want to customize your own. Regardless of the changes that you make to the content of your sessions, it is important to keep the structure consistent from week to week because this creates safety and cohesion for the girls.

Deciding the group rules

Many facilitators involve the girls in the process of deciding the group rules because this builds group cohesion. They often make suggestions—such as listening with respect, privacy and how to use the Talking Stick—but leave the final decision and wording up to the girls. It's a good idea to write down the rules so that they can be read out each week. The rules should be simple so that the girls can follow them and few in number so that girls don't feel that they are constantly in danger of failing.

Creating an atmosphere of safety

Each week the facilitators remind the girls that they cannot fail in this group. They assure them that what they have to say is important because it lets other girls know that they are not alone in how they feel. They explain the *grungies* and repeat the group rules. While this may seem repetitious, it makes the girls feel safe because they know that what is expected of them won't change and this establishes a sense of continuity from session to session. During adolescence, girls look outside themselves for behavioral cues, so creating a consistent environment allows them to put their energy into becoming aware of their own experiences and thoughts instead of worrying about being criticized for doing something wrong.

Facilitators use their first names in the group and include some personal information when they introduce themselves to the girls. In group discussions, they share experiences they have had that are common to the ones that the girls are describing. This helps to establish an atmosphere of informality and creates an egalitarian atmosphere in the group—one that is more in keeping with the relational way in which girls learn.

While the facilitators encourage the development of intimacy among the girls, they discourage group hugs. This is because girls who have been sexually abused have difficulty being touched, no matter how gentle or caring the intent. As well, girls from different cultural backgrounds have different boundaries regarding physical contact.

Learning about the *grungies*

JUST FOR GIRLS helps girls decode the language of fat by making them aware of what they tell themselves when they are feeling down, and providing them with an alternative means of expression. It does this by teaching girls about the *grungies*—a term coined to describe the things that girls say to themselves that make them feel badly about themselves. The *grungies* are a **key element** of the program. If girls do not decode their *grungies* then they are likely to deal with their discomfort around feeling fat by dieting and by experimenting in eating disorder behaviors. They are also more likely to internalize their distress, which makes them vulnerable to depression and thoughts of suicide. By learning to decode the language of fat, girls are better able to express their thoughts and feelings, and retain their voices and their sense of self.

In grades five and six *grungies* often center around 'feeling stupid' and anything else that makes girls different from their friends—such as 'feeling too tall,' 'too short,' or being the only person to have curly hair. While some of these girls 'feel fat,' most of them associate fat with their mothers. By grade seven most girls 'feel fat,' with 'feeling stupid' coming in second.

Each group session begins with a *grungie circle*. Handout H-5 will help you explain what a *grungie* is. Because girls in grades five and six take longer to make the connection between the *grungies* and their experiences, the facilitator encourages them to talk about the things that aggravate them, bug them and make them feel badly. Older girls (and younger girls who grasp the concept) are asked to remember a time the previous week when they were 'hit by a *grungie*.' They pay attention to the time of day, the activity they were involved in, the thoughts they were thinking and whatever feelings they had that they are aware of. In doing this they shift their focus away from 'fat (stupid, ugly, etc.) and become curious about whatever it is that lies beneath. Girls then retell the stories about their *grungie*, this time leaving out feeling fat or stupid and focusing instead on the feelings and experiences that are of real concern to them.

The facilitator validates the girls' feelings and stories. She lets the girls know that they have a right to their feelings and that they are not alone in how they feel. She helps them understand why they feel the way that they do, reframing their stories and concerns in relation to the female gender culture. Teaching them about 'girl things' provides them with an understanding of the societal pressures that they face. For example, fifteen year old Amy talked about 'feeling fat' when she was with her friends. In the retelling of her story, she recognized that she felt insecure because there were more than two others girls present. When the facilitator helped her understand that feeling uncomfortable in large groups was a 'girl thing,' Amy was assured that there was nothing wrong or abnormal about her. This allowed her to express her feelings directly and then begin to deal with them constructively.

When eleven year old Lindsay felt fat, the facilitator and the group helped her connect her *grungie* to her feelings about wearing a skimpy costume at her dance recital the week before. Berating herself that she should be feeling good that people were looking at her, she encoded her discomfort in the language of fat. Lindsay felt less alone when the other girls shared similar feelings at having their bodies on display. The ensuing discussion about how girls are objectified in the media and in turn are expected to objectify themselves gave the girls a context for the shame that they felt at being looked at, especially when their bodies didn't match what society considers the ideal. It is through the telling and validation of their stories, by reclaiming their female culture and by understanding societal pressures that girls are able to develop and retain their voices and their selves.

Using the Talking Stick

The Talking Stick is a custom that is practiced by First Nations (Indian) people all over Turtle Island (North America). It has been handed down from generation to generation. Many West Coast tribes use an actual carved stick, although the Talking Stick may also take other forms such as a feather or a rock. While the custom of the Talking Stick can vary from tribe to tribe, in the custom described here it is passed counter-clockwise (or to the left) by the person in charge of the Talking Circle. The person who holds the Talking Stick can speak about any topic without interruption. Whatever the person says will not leave the Circle because the Circle cannot be broken. When the speaker is finished she says, "all my relations" and passes the Talking Stick to the next person. If the next person does not wish to speak, she can just say "all my relations" and pass the Talking Stick along. The phrase "all my relations" reminds the speaker of who she is, of her relationships with her family and her relatives, of her extended relationship with all human beings as well as with fish and birds and trees, all the animate and inanimate forms that can be seen or imagined and of her responsibility to them as well as to herself.

JUST FOR GIRLS borrowed the custom of the Talking Stick because it is a very powerful way of providing girls with a voice and of validating the importance of relationships in their lives. The Talking Stick ensures that the girls will speak one at a time—the girl who holds the stick has the floor. This teaches girls to consider what they have to say as serious when they are speaking and to respect each other when they are listening. The program has modified the custom so that after each girl has had a turn, girls don't have to follow the continuity of the circle and can hand the Talking Stick to anyone who wants to speak. As well, instead of remaining silent throughout, the facilitator can respond in order to provide each girl with feedback, validate her experience, and complete the kind of responsive interaction that is needed to make the speaker feel safe.

You can use any symbolic object to represent the Talking Stick—some groups use a baton, others a 'talk rock.' Introducing its use may initially be difficult—the girls are used to talking as one large group, and it's hard for them to focus on themselves individually. Eventually they begin to understand that they each have a right to be heard, and that the other girls will listen just because they hold the Talking Stick. When girls realize that they will all have an opportunity to speak, it's easier for them to be patient and to plan what they will say in their turn. The Talking Stick gives them time not only to tell their stories, but also to elaborate on the details and their perceptions of the implications. It validates not only what they have to say but also how they choose to say it.

There is a secondary benefit to using the Talking Stick. It is so easy to fall into the trap of trying to 'discipline' the girls—especially if you are a teacher or a former teacher, as I am. We have a tendency to ensure that girls listen and don't talk all at once by telling them to be mature and to behave themselves, and by threatening to revoke certain privileges if they don't comply. When we do this, girls may respond by engaging us in a power struggle or else by being 'nice' while at the same time shutting us out from their thoughts and opinions. Using the Talking Stick not only reinforces the idea that everyone has something important to say and deserves to be heard, it ensures the girls' cooperation in an equal and respectful way.

Choosing topics for discussion

Some facilitators structure each group session around issues that arise in the *grungie* circle that week. In order to do this, however, you need to be familiar with all the topics and their background material and with the activities—something that comes with a great deal of experience. Other facilitators plan what they are going to do ahead of time so that they can learn about the topic and prepare any materials that they may want to use.

In some groups the facilitators chose all of the topics. Others involve the girls in deciding upon the issues that they want to address. Having the girls make these decisions gives them ownership of the group and therefore enhances their learning experience.

Involving Girls in the Planning

- Suggest topics that you think might interest the girls. Include ones that are relevant to their developmental stage. Write them on a flip chart. Ask the girls to suggest other topics.

- Give each girl an index card or piece of paper, and ask each girl to list the three topics or concerns that she would most like the group to talk about.

- Collect the cards and add their choices to the flip chart. The anonymity allows girls to write what they really want instead of looking to the other girls for what's 'right.' Since most girls want to talk about boys, giving them more than one choice ensures that other topics will also be considered.

- Have the girls weight the importance of each topic by voting on them. Holding up five fingers means that they want to talk about the topic a lot; three fingers indicates 'somewhat' and one finger indicates 'just a bit.'

- Plan the sessions according to the results of the vote, beginning with the most important topics first.

- As the program progresses, check to see if the topics that the girls voted on in the beginning are still of importance to them now.

You might want to consider leaving one session as a 'free' session so that the girls have the opportunity to ask questions that might have come up for them around material discussed in previous sessions or about issues that have not yet been addressed. The week before the free session, ask the girls to write their questions on an index card or piece of paper. This gives them anonymity and therefore safety and gives you the time to gather the information that they might need.

If you would like to use this group as a way of addressing other issues such as smoking, teen pregnancy, abusive relationships, sexually transmitted diseases or other topics relevant to your mandate or to the girls in your group, plan one or two sessions specifically around these topics and integrate these topics into other sessions when it is appropriate.

Integrating girls' developmental issues

JUST FOR GIRLS has been designed for girls in early and middle adolescence, although you can adapt your sessions for use with pre-adolescent girls and with young women. Most of the time the girls themselves raise the issues that are relevant to their specific developmental stages because these are ones that are of immediate concern to them. However, if the girls do not bring up these issues, you might want to integrate them into your sessions.

Early Adolescence: Developmental Issues
(around 11 to 13 years of age)

✓ Social, emotional and physical changes that occur during puberty
✓ Early bloomers and late bloomers
✓ Transition to high school
✓ Changing dynamics of friendships—teasing, exclusion, secrets
✓ Teasing and bullying
✓ Interest in boys
✓ Problems with parents
✓ School pressures

Middle Adolescence: Developmental Issues
(around 14 to 16 years old)

✓ Increasing independence—how to achieve autonomy and still maintain connection
✓ Anxiety about friendships
✓ Boys and sexuality
✓ Pressure to achieve
✓ Pressure to be perfect (i.e. thin and confident)

As you plan your groups I suggest that you include one or more sessions on body image and body awareness, and focus on the pressure for girls to be thin. If you are facilitating a group of girls who are in early adolescence, I suggest that you also include a session on puberty. If your group is made up of middle-adolescent girls it is a good idea to spend extra time on friendships and on teaching communication skills.

Choosing activities that encourage self-expression

While a certain amount of discussion goes on in the group, especially in the *grungie circle*, facilitators include different activities in order to encourage different forms of self-expression and to give girls an opportunity to learn and try out new skills and behaviors. The section entitled CONTEXT provides you with background information about the issues that are of concern to girls and a range of activities to address each issue.

Activities such as role-playing help deflect the energy of younger girls who begin to squirm after about twenty or thirty minutes, and facilitate skill-building for the older ones. Girls can use role-playing to act out their *grungies*. The girls are divided into smaller groups. In each group one girl is chosen to act out her story. The other members of the group become the cast as she instructs them on their role. Coaching the other girls in her group—as well as performing her own part—allows each actor to make her experiences concrete and therefore to take them seriously. The girls in the 'audience' are important because they bear witness to and, therefore, validate both the feelings and the event. Girls are encouraged to change the endings on their *grungies* and to express their real feelings instead of 'feeling fat.'

Role-playing helps girls act out situations that are difficult for them, such as when they wanted to say no but were afraid of physical harm or of hurting someone's feelings. This helps girls practice assertive behavior. Girls also use role-playing as a way of acting out conflicts and practicing communication skills. Role-playing allows girls to deal with their feelings in a direct and constructive way and to try out new situations and practice new behaviors in a safe environment. It also helps them feel more positive about themselves.

JUST FOR GIRLS makes use of movement, art and writing as additional means of self-expression. Movement and body drawings foster body awareness and help girls regain the kinesthetic experience of their bodies. They also teach girls to relate to their bodies other than through their external image. Artwork and writing helps girls express their feelings and share their ideas. In one group the girls created an ongoing advice column in order to deal with issues that were important to them such as family conflict, friends, boys and their weight issues. Care must be taken when you use art as an activity that you praise the girls for their insights—not for the artwork itself—and that you do not try to interpret their work.

The girls in each group are given a journal and encouraged to write stories about what's underneath their *grungies* so that they can express their feelings rather than transform them into feeling fat. The facilitator of one grade six group organized the journal into topics and activities to make it more structured for the girls. In a grade eight group the facilitator set aside time each week for girls to write in their journals. Facilitators of other groups have left the journals totally up to the discretion of the girls.

Some girls decorate their journals, put pictures in them and draw in them. Some girls write poetry. One girl used her journal to write a book. Each week she read a new chapter to the group. While the girls encourage each other to share their journals, it is important for them to recognize that their journals are private and that they have a choice about what to share or whether they want to share at all. It is also important for us to recognize their privacy and respect their boundaries. In one group the co-facilitator became so concerned that the girls should be 'paying attention and learning' that she asked them to hand in their journals so that she could grade them at the end of the session. This destroyed the group process and broke the connection that the facilitator had with the group.

Respecting the needs of the girls

No matter how well you organize your group and plan your sessions, you need to be prepared to put these plans aside in order to meet the immediate needs of the girls. Sometimes it takes more than one session to cover a topic if the girls still have concerns, and if the topic is especially important to them. In one grade eight group the facilitators spent numerous sessions teaching girls communication skills so that they could deal with the conflicts they were experiencing in their friendships. Sometimes girls raise issues that are immediate and urgent and they pre-empt whatever plans you have made. In one grade seven group the girls were upset because their male teacher had made comments about girls' breasts. This led into an unplanned discussion about sexual harassment, which was more relevant to them that day than the topic that had been planned.

Sometimes the entire direction of the group changes. The girls in one inner city school came from such poverty and neglect that the facilitators spent the entire twelve weeks teaching them basic skills for taking care of themselves. This included encouraging them to brush their teeth and take a bath. The facilitator of a grade eight group knew that she had to change directions when one of the girls asked, 'How can we worry about the *grungies* when we're afraid of getting beat up after school?'

Balancing process and structure

As you facilitate your group it is important that you continuously find a balance between the process that is at the heart of the program and the structure that allows for the development of skills. If there is too much emphasis on the process—that is, on encouraging girls to express themselves—then the program cannot teach them skills or provide them with an opportunity to try out new behavior. If you get too caught up on structure and are concerned that they are not learning enough, then you run the risk of sacrificing the girls' voices and experiences to activities that center around problem-solving. Please keep this in mind when you use the SESSION PLANS—there are times when you will not be able to do all of the activities. In one grade seven group that I was facilitating, the co-facilitator that I was training became upset over the amount of time that the girls took to draw their bodies. 'I wouldn't do it again. The girls wasted too much time talking.' Because she prided herself on getting things done, it was difficult for her at first to understand that the talking that the girls were doing was a necessary part of the process of working cooperatively and supporting each other.

Handling difficult situations

Although most groups go smoothly, difficult situations do sometimes arise. Facilitators need to know what to do:

- *When Someone Monopolizes the Discussion*

Every time a certain girl is handed the Talking Stick in the *grungie* circle, she continues to speak endlessly. On one hand you want to respect the tradition of the Talking Stick and allow her the right to speak. On the other hand, you become concerned that she is monopolizing all of the time. You might want to say something to her such as: 'It sounds as if you have a lot to say, Elizabeth, and what you really have to say is really important. Maybe you can pick the most important thing, and then talk about the next important thing when the Talking Stick is passed back to you.' If she still doesn't respond after you have made this suggestion several times, then you might have a different girl be the time keeper each session and limit the amount of time that each girl receives.

- *When Someone Won't Respect the Rules*

Because the girls are involved in making the rules, they often reinforce them by calling attention to those who break them: those who interrupt frequently, call out a lot, don't use the Talking Stick, and have difficulty sitting still during the *grungie* circle. Sometimes, however, there is one girl in the group who is constantly disruptive. Her behavior is not only uncomfortable, it makes the group unsafe for the other girls. In this situation you might want to describe her behavior to the disruptive girl, describe the effects of her behavior and let her know that it is disrespectful to the other girls. Unless she can be respectful, she will have to leave the group for that session. For example, you might say something like: 'When you call out all the time, Mary, you are telling the person who is speaking that what she has to say is not important. That is not respectful to her or to the other girls. It is very important that we are respectful to one another. If it is hard for you to be respectful today, then I'd like you to leave the group and to try again next week.'

Facilitators rarely have to ask a girl to leave the group. If you do, however, it is important that you discuss the situation afterwards with the girls. While some may feel relieved that the disruptive girl is gone, they also empathize with how she might be feeling. Because they often focus on the other person's feelings at the expense of their own, they might see your actions as unfair. You need to reassure them that they can feel relieved and also feel bad for the girl who was asked to leave.

- *When Someone Begins to Cry*

Because girls are talking about issues that concern them, it is not uncommon that someone will begin to cry. Sometimes we hug her—more out of our need than hers. If we feel uncomfortable and don't know what to do, we try to make the feelings go away by minimizing them or by trying to make her feel better. Sometimes we tend to focus all of the attention on her and encourage her to explore her feelings in more depth. None of these responses are appropriate. When someone cries it is important that we allow her to have her feelings, but then we need to move on to the next person.

If someone begins to cry, pass the box of tissues to her and say something such as: 'This must have been very hurtful' or 'This must be very painful.' You might want to say something such as: 'Hurtful or painful things often happen. It's good to get the feelings out.' Take the focus off her to allow her the privacy and dignity of her feelings. If her feelings relate to a difficult situation at home or a painful experience (such as a death in the family, loss of a pet or friendship, divorce, sexual or physical abuse), then you might say to her: 'I can see that this is very important to you and is very painful. Perhaps it is something that we can spend time on in private during the break or after the session.'

Helping girls support each other

Adolescence is a time when girls may experience dramatic changes in their friendships. In early adolescence, girls deal with the dark side of friendship in the form of secrets, exclusion and teasing. In middle adolescence, girls' alliances frequently shift causing them to experience anxiety about the stability of their friendships and their own adequacy as a friend. *JUST FOR GIRLS* encourages the mutually responsive relationships that girls develop with each other and provides them with the skills necessary to maintain and/or repair them. The section entitled CONTEXT will help you teach girls communication skills so that they can express themselves without worrying about hurting each other or 'taking care of' the other person, and so that they can resolve conflicts between themselves. It will help you teach girls about boundaries, about supporting and helping their friends in a way that empowers both girls, and of the dangers of over-helping their friends at the expense of themselves. When you as facilitators share your own experiences with the girls you model a relational way of being that is based on honesty and mutuality.

Closing the session—giving feedback

Regardless of the time constraints that may arise, each group needs to have closure. Facilitators often spend this time on an activity that builds self-esteem. Because girls in our society are encouraged to value themselves according to how they look, little attention is paid to the qualities, characteristics, skills and talents that make them unique. One of the ways of countering the emphasis on looks is to help girls build up a corresponding 'bank account' of things that they value about themselves. Giving and receiving feedback is a good way to do this. At the end of each session, each girl is asked to name something about herself—such as something that makes her interesting or that makes her a good friend. Initially this is difficult for girls who are used to thinking about themselves in negative terms. Girls are also asked to give verbal bouquets to each other. Feedback exercises give girls a broader framework in which to see each other and themselves. Along with their relational qualities, girls are encouraged to include other qualities such as creativity, courageousness, honesty, and intelligence. This helps counteract the tendency that girls have to define themselves and each other in terms of 'pretty' and 'nice.'

FACILITATING YOUR OWN GROUP

JUST FOR GIRLS has been designed for use by women of different professional and lay orientations, and with different levels of experience and skill. While it helps to have basic group facilitation skills and/or a co-facilitator to help you and to share things with as the group goes along, you don't need four PhD's or yet another intensive training course. The most essential ingredients that you bring to the group are your own experiences of growing up female and the common gender dynamics and characteristics that you share with girls. What is most important is your ability to *schmooze* with them—your willingness to model healthy female relationships by engaging honestly with girls, by letting them know what you think and what you feel, and sharing your own experiences of the world instead of telling them what to do.

Sharing yourself with the girls

One of the most powerful ways for us to share ourselves with girls is to *schmooze* with them. *Schmoozing* is a term that describes a communication ritual that all of us are familiar with in our interactions with other women. When I have a problem, for example, I telephone a friend. Putting the problem into words makes it real. This is important because many of us tend to minimize our experiences. My friend usually says things such as 'Ooh, that's terrible, that's really difficult, I can't believe it, you must be so upset!' Her empathic response validates my feelings and lets me know that I have a right to the way I feel. My friend then shares a similar problem of her own and if she doesn't have one, she shares someone else's. This lets me know that I am normal and that other people have similar experiences. Later, she might give me feedback or brainstorm strategies with me. When I hang up the phone, the problem might still be there, but expressing it and having it validated and normalized makes me feel better about myself and makes the problem easier to resolve.

As adults we *schmooze* mainly with other adults. We rarely *schmooze* with girls. One reason is that as girls approach adolescence we begin to worry about the dangers that they face. In our worst nightmare we envision depressed, violent girls with eating disorders who are smoking, having unsafe sex and getting into cars with abusive boys who are drunk—all in the same week! Because we want to prevent girls from succumbing to the risks that we know that they face and in our urgency to keep them safe, we *talk at* them with warnings instead of *listening to* them. Instead of responding to our 'wisdom' and reaping the benefits of our experiences, girls distance themselves from us and tune us out.

Facilitating a group for girls requires that we adults bring our personal selves into our professional lives. Girls are more willing to communicate when we share ourselves with them. This does not mean that we tell them about our messy divorce or use them as a sounding board for issues that we are still in the process of working out. It means that we share similar experiences of ours as a way of normalizing theirs, of giving them permission to raise certain topics, and of giving them language to help them when they have trouble describing what they feel. By sharing our experiences with girls we validate theirs and form a connection with them that facilitates their growth.

Sharing ourselves with girls can be difficult for those of us who have been trained to view our professionalism as based on hierarchy and on distance. Remembering our own adolescence can be painful for some of us because it brings up memories that we consider best left forgotten. Often we don't share our experiences with girls because we are afraid to 'burden' them. We think that if we don't talk to girls about the guys who dumped us we will spare them that pain. By not talking with girls of our experiences, we rob them of a context for their own. We send them into the uncharted territory of adolescence all alone. Instead of giving them support, we set them adrift.

The stories that girls tell deal with issues that are the same (or very similar) to the ones that we constantly deal with as grown women. They talk about relationships, and their difficulties in being true to themselves while not hurting anyone else. They talk about the pain of rejection and how hard it is to be regarded as different. They talk about sexuality and harassment and their ambivalent feelings about their changing bodies. They talk about taking care of others and not getting their own needs met. And while we want to validate their experiences by sharing our own, it's not easy when the issues that girls raise are the ones that are so emotionally charged for us, or when their value systems or means of coping are very different from ours.

As facilitators we must constantly try to understand what life looks like for girls—to continuously ask them about their feelings and what their experiences mean to them in the context of their lives. We need to monitor ourselves for commonalties where we relate to the girls, and when we don't relate to their experiences we still need to validate them without judging them or minimizing their feelings or fixing things. In one group that I was facilitating one of the girls shared her experiences of growing up in Ethiopia and seeing her parents killed. All that I could do was listen to her and validate her feelings. She didn't need me to fix it. She needed to tell her story so that she could bear witness to her life.

Facilitating a group for girls makes us take stock of our *shoulds*—we *should* always be right, know the answer, agree with other people, be patient, share when we don't want to, never get angry, never say no. When we turn off our heads and open our hearts, we know when we feel connected to someone else and when we feel safe, heard, understood and accepted—regardless of whether they agree with us or not. When that connection is broken, we feel abandoned, judged, wronged and criticized. Girls respond when they feel an emotional bond with women who are honest about their feelings and opinions. We don't always have to know the answer, or be patient, or agree with their behavior or points of view—as long as we are honest in our interactions with them. We lose them the moment that we cease to be ourselves. When we assume our formal and authoritative 'adult voices' we become part of the dominant culture. The girls close down and begin either to act out or to become *nice*. They also don't come back to the group.

Acknowledging our own weight prejudice

Facilitating a group means being able to acknowledge our own weight prejudice and monitoring our language and actions for signs of it. As women who work with girls we are also products of the culture in which girls mature and we are influenced by these same pressures. Despite our best intentions, we pass our attitudes along to the girls. The girls in one group talked about a well-meaning teacher who brought cookies in for the class. Realizing that there were not enough to go around, the teacher said, 'Only the thin kids will get cookies. The fat kids don't need them.'

As facilitators, we must be able to accept a range of body types and sizes. This means that we do not fall prey to the myth that equates being fat with being unhealthy, or the myth that everyone wants to be thin—and can be if they try hard enough. We need to value our bodies as functional and beautiful, no matter what size they are. We must also be able to value people for who they are and what they have to offer. Because we are constantly bombarded by the same messages from the media as the girls, we must consciously question, negate and refute those images of perfection and what they mean.

Most of us struggle to varying degrees with our natural bodies. When we share this struggle with girls we validate theirs. However, when we lose the battle and become preoccupied with food and weight then it is not appropriate for us to work with pre-adolescent and adolescent girls. If you see fat as bad, if you are presently dieting, or if you have a strong belief that losing weight and eating only healthy food and being in shape will change your life (or the lives of others) then this group is not for you. If you are recovering from an eating disorder then you need to take stock of your unresolved issues and carefully examine your attitudes towards food and weight. Despite our best intentions, we often make our issues the issues of the group. While this group is not about eating disorders, it is difficult to help girls accept their natural bodies if in our hearts we still believe that these bodies are the wrong size and shape.

Supporting girls as they try out new behavior

In teaching girls the skills that divert them from succumbing to the risks of adolescence, we introduce them to an image of women that is different from that prevailing in our society. We offer them dynamic choices instead of the mantle of passivity and self-repression and self-control that they are expected to assume as they grow up. However, in encouraging girls to be assertive and in steering them back to their own culture, we put them at risk of disapproval and reaction from their parents, their teachers and their friends. If we are going to teach girls new behaviors and encourage them to practice a different way of being in the world, then we must also be there to give them support. This means that we must be willing to be advocates for them when they need it. For example, two of the girls in a grade seven group that I co-facilitated complained about being sexually harassed by their teacher. The co-facilitator and I encouraged the girls to talk to the school principal, helped them role-play what they wanted to say to her and then worked with the principal in order to resolve the situation.

We need to model the same behaviors that we are teaching the girls. It is up to us as women who work with them and care for them to provide them with a solid foundation for their roots. We must nourish them with understanding and acceptance so that they can grow to their full potential as women and take their places as equals in the world.

Trusting yourself

The *JUST FOR GIRLS* program is flexible. No two groups are alike nor are any two facilitators. Some facilitators are more interested in art, some in writing or drama; others prefer a little of each. If you are facilitating the group for the first time, please remember that you cannot fail if you are open and curious and not obsessed with your own weight. As women we learn from hands-on experience and from trial and error. If one activity doesn't work, then try another.

When women are asked what they liked best about facilitating a group, most of them say that it is the experience of learning about girls from the girls. Instead of approaching each session with the fear of doing something wrong, try looking at the whole process with curiosity. After each session ask yourself what you learned from the girls and what you learned about yourself. This will help you trust yourself and let go of your need to do everything perfectly the first time. As you become more comfortable facilitating groups you will gradually develop your own style and make the program your own.

What Experienced Facilitators Have To Say:

» Eight sessions are not quite enough. Neither is just an hour per session. If that's all that you have, do the group anyway—but try somehow to add in extra time.

» Plan your session so that you're prepared, but don't expect to do everything that you've planned.

» Don't plan too much. The girls need time to process the information and their feelings.

» Spend a lot of time on relationships. That is what is of most importance to the girls.

» Let the girls lead the group. Have a basic plan but be prepared to change it.

» Invite the girls to state the issues that they would like to discuss and bring the list out from time to time for them to add or delete topics. You can give them suggestions that help them get started, but let them make it their agenda.

» Make sure that you are in a location where you will not be interrupted.

» Make sure that your co-facilitator is someone you know and work with. It's difficult to facilitate with someone from another program or with someone whose views are different from yours.

» Use graduates of the groups as peer group mentors the next year.

» Set up a buddy system between elementary school girls and middle school or junior high/high school girls. This helps make their transition easier.

» If you want to attract junior high, high school girls or young college women, find a trendy name and *don't* mention weight, body image or eating disorders.

» Not every group works! In a group that was made up of First Nation girls and Caucasian girls, the girls split into two groups and nothing could get them together. Finally the group had to be split into two.

» The best part of doing the group is getting to know the girls better, and seeing them change as they grow.

EVALUATION

During the first session of the group we ask the girls to fill in an information sheet because we want to know something about them. We tell them that they can look at the sheet at the end of the program to see if they feel differently about themselves. **Handout H-4** the *Tell Us About You Form* contains a scale to measure the degree to which girls feel fat or stupid, and another to measure self-esteem.

During the last session of the program, the girls are asked to fill out **Handout H-6**. The *Feedback Form* asks them to describe what they liked and did not like about the group, which activities were most useful and least useful, and the changes that they see in themselves. They are also asked to talk about the changes that they see in each other. We don't use the word *evaluation* because it has pass/fail connotations. The *Feedback Form* contains the same scales that were used in the first session so that the facilitators as well as the girls can see what changes took place.

Feedback is important for two reasons. As facilitators we need to know about the program from the girls' perspective. We need to know what they understood and what they missed about certain concepts, what they found helpful and what they had difficulty with, and whether or not any kind of change actually occurred. This helps us decide what information and activities to retain and which to change the next time we run the group.

Asking girls to fill out the *Feedback Form* also lets them know that we value their ideas enough to incorporate them into future groups. Filling out the form provides girls with the opportunity to articulate what they learned and how they learned it, what they found helpful and where their areas of difficulty lay. The more feedback that girls give and receive, and the more precisely they can articulate their own experiences, the more they are able to perceive and value themselves in ways other than through how they look. In learning to pay attention to their own needs, girls reinforce a sense of themselves that is grounded in their own experience.

Girls write about being less shy and less embarrassed and more assertive at the end of the group. They are more able to speak their minds. They see that knowing about the *grungies* is helpful because this means they don't have to feel badly about themselves. While girls often describe certain activities that they have enjoyed, the most important part of the group is always the opportunity to talk about their concerns and to know that other girls feel the same way.

COORDINATING PREVENTION EFFORTS WITH SCHOOL

Whether the group is held on or off the premises, it is important to have the cooperation of the teachers and the administration of the schools that the girls attend. The school can arrange initial contact with the girls by allowing facilitators to come invite girls to the group. If the school supports the program, then class time can often be arranged in which to hold the group. The school can make referrals, recommend the group to parents, and reinforce the skills that the girls are taught.

Before the group begins it is important to speak to the principal and to the teachers of the targeted grade in order to describe the program and address any concerns that they might have. If you feel comfortable doing so and if it is appropriate, you can hold an informal presentation for the staff during lunch or recess or during one of their professional days. When I do presentations to teachers I include some information about female development and about male/female gender cultures in order to give them a context for why girls feel fat. I talk about the *grungies* and how to deal with them and about the issues and concerns that girls raise. I also invite the staff to examine their own attitudes towards girls and towards weight prejudice.

Sometimes schools are reluctant to offer support for the *JUST FOR GIRLS* program because it is just for girls and therefore excludes the boys. Teachers want to include the boys in the group because they want them to receive the same information as girls and want them to learn about girls so that they will stop teasing them. When the question 'But what about the boys?' arises it is important to differentiate between the different kinds of learning that adolescents participate in. While all adolescents would benefit from learning about gender differences and developing better communication skills, the purpose of the *JUST FOR GIRLS* program is so that girls can learn about themselves in the context of their female culture. When even one boy is introduced to the group, no matter how 'sensitive' he is, the dynamics change and the girls silence themselves. My suggestion is to develop parallel programs for boys which men can facilitate in order to provide boys with good male role models. It is important that these programs are grounded in male culture and are therefore more likely to address the needs of boys. [The section JUST FOR BOYS addresses what is needed for boys.]

How schools can help girls

Schools can play a vital role in helping girls make a healthy transition through adolescence by incorporating the philosophy and skills of the *JUST FOR GIRLS* program into the school structure and curriculum. The school administration, staff, and parents need to be involved in order to do this.

What Schools Can Do

✓ Teach girls and boys about the *grungies* before adolescence so that they will have developed good coping skills when they need them.

✓ Help girls and boys become aware of when they have been 'hit by a *grungie*' inside and outside the classroom and encourage them to express the feelings and talk about the situations underneath.

✓ Pay attention to attitudes towards fat prejudice and how they affect interaction with students. For example, how often is a fat student chosen as a monitor?

✓ Encourage acceptance of a range of body types on an ongoing basis. For example, structure physical education activities so that it includes all body types.

✓ Encourage diversity. Put up posters of active girls and women as well as boys and men of all sizes, races and abilities and disabilities.

✓ Teach students about both gender cultures and the differences in behavior between girls and guys. This is especially important in the junior high and high schools.

✓ Validate both gender cultures. For example, point out 'girl things' and 'guy things.'

✓ When giving girls feedback about their work, stress what is positive about what they have done before you make suggestions for change.

✓ Give girls feedback about skills and qualities that do not focus on their appearance or on being 'nice.'

✓ Give boys feedback that reinforces relational qualities as well as their sense of adequacy.

✓ Help girls and boys develop an awareness of the individual ways in which they learn.

✓ Teach conflict resolution and communication skills to students on an ongoing basis as part of the elementary, middle school, junior and high school curriculum.

✓ Help girls recognize and deal with the dark side of friendship such as exclusion and secrets. Help boys deal with anger management.

✓ Teach girls and boys how to deal with teasing and bullying.

✓ Institute and enforce no-bullying and no-sexual harassment policies in your elementary, middle, junior and high schools.

CONTEXT

This section presents background information and activities for many of the issues that girls raise. It will help you structure your groups. I have tried wherever possible to include some societal or behavioral context. Some of this information may be new to you, or you may find that in some areas your experience and knowledge is greater than mine—or that you disagree with my point of view. My recent book *When Girls Feel Fat* elaborates upon these issues in greater detail. It is listed in the RESOURCES section along with other books, programs and videos that provide background information on these topics. In some of the following sections, I have included questions that girls in various groups have asked in order to give you a sense of what it is they want to know. This section is intended as a resource for facilitators—so feel free to add to it, or leave out the parts that make you uncomfortable.

Learning activities

The *learning activities* can be used to stimulate discussion. In most cases, I have provided a 'menu' of activities for each topic. You don't have to use the activities on the menu, nor do you have to use all of them. Feel free to add some of your own. The first time you facilitate a group you might want to stick to what's comfortable. Some of the activities probe more deeply into the emotional lives of girls than do others. They require a certain amount of counseling skill and experience which you might not have, or may just be in the process of acquiring. Some of the topics will be more relevant to one group than to another. You might find that some of the activities are more appropriate than others for the age group that you are facilitating. It is only after you begin to facilitate a group that you really develop a sense of what works for you as well as what works for the girls.

I have included activities in the REPRODUCIBLE HANDOUTS that you can use with your groups. Having information that is written down can be useful to girls who are visual learners, and who might want to refer back to these concepts later on. Written activities can be helpful because they give girls quiet time to think about themselves. Care must be taken; however, to remind girls (and to remind ourselves) that they cannot fail the activities and that these do not replace discussion about their real life experiences.

I have arranged the subjects in the diagram *Building a Healthy Sense of Self* into learning activities, which proceed from the most personal to the societal. Central to the individual is her sense of *SELF* and her *SELF ESTEEM*. Next are her *FEELINGS*. Then comes her *BODY* and the changes she experiences as she moves into puberty, her *BODY IMAGE*—the physical and emotional experience of her own body and her relationship to the food that she uses to nourish herself. Each girl is situated in a *FAMILY*. Of next greatest importance to her are *RELATIONSHIPS*. These include her friendships, her developing sexuality, her changing relationships with boys and her communication skills. At this point in her development, every girl's life is strongly influenced by her experiences in *SCHOOL* and in the immediate *COMMUNITY*—especially any experiences of bullying, teasing and/or harassment. Everything, of course, takes place in the context of the *SOCIETY* in which we all live.

SELF

Our *self* is like a prism. The different roles that we play and the situations that we find ourselves in combined with the thoughts, feelings, opinions and perceptions that we have at any particular moment make up the various sides. We show these different sides of ourselves to different people. Our parents, for example, almost never see us in the same way that our friends do. Because we never show all of our sides at once, no one side defines us. Instead, the various aspects of ourselves fit together to make up a whole.

We learn about our self or about *who we are* through hearing what other people say about us, identifying what we ourselves feel and value, and thinking about our *selves* in relationship with others. Being in touch with our selves means knowing what we think and feel at any given time. It means being able to form perceptions about others instead of worrying about what they think of us.

In adolescence, many girls withhold their feelings and their opinions in order to be kind and nice. The more they move away from being the center of their own experience in order to please other people, the more they lose of their *sense-of-self*. In our groups we help girls regain and retain their sense-of-self by giving them the skills to refocus on the 'I' instead of on the 'You.' We do this by helping them to gather information and to be as articulate about their *selves* as they can.

Building a Healthy Sense of Self (Handout H-7)

The diagram helps girls understand how each of us lives within the context of (and is affected by our relationship with) all of the other components of the diagram. Go through the diagram beginning with *SELF* and ask girls to suggest issues and concerns that affect each section.

Personal Symbol

- Bring something to the group, which represents how you see yourself.
- This symbol can be subject to change as the group progresses.

Your Name

[Note: You might want to keep handy a book that has a list of the meanings of names.]

◆ What does it mean?
◆ How was it chosen?
◆ Does anybody else in your family have the same name?
◆ Do you have a nickname? Where does it come from?
◆ Have you ever been teased about your name?
◆ Have you ever gone through a period when you didn't like it very much?
◆ If you could choose another name, what would it be?

If you have girls in your group from a variety of ethnic backgrounds, invite these girls to teach their names to the group and allow the group time to practice getting them right.

Your Origin/Culture

◆ What race/ethnicity are you?
◆ Where does your family come from?
◆ How many different countries can you trace your history to?
◆ What different languages does your family speak?
◆ What do you know about them?
◆ Who do you look like?
◆ Where does that person come from?

Describe a Typical Day in Your Life

◆ Who/what are the people, objects, places, and situations that are important to you?
◆ Which of the situations are most likely to produce a *grungie*?

Shoe Box (Ongoing Activity)

◆ On the inside, put all of the things that describe or symbolize how you see yourself, your hopes, your dreams, and your fears.
◆ Decorate the shoe box on the outside with how others (parents, teachers, peers) see you, and with the expectations that they have of you and how they expect you to be.

SELF-ESTEEM

The term *self-esteem* refers to how we feel about ourselves, either positively or negatively. Healthy self-esteem is the capacity to think of yourself warmly and worthy even when you make a mistake. Until the age of ten girls tend to have high self-esteem if they have not been sexually or physically abused, witnessed violence first-hand or experienced intense emotional trauma such as their parents' divorce. When girls enter adolescence their self-esteem begins to drop. Many girls begin to place their entire self-esteem on their external image, because our society encourages girls to value themselves in terms of how they look. Since very few people ever meet the societal ideal, girls are set up from the beginning to feel badly about themselves.

In our groups we help girls build up a 'bank' of positive self-esteem points by encouraging them to become aware of and to value their other qualities, characteristics, skills and talents. We also add positive points by giving them descriptive feedback, and by teaching them to give feedback to each other. You can use the activities that I've described here at the end of each group. Receiving positive feedback allows girls to leave the group feeling good about themselves.

Valuing My Personal Strengths (Handout H-8)

Some girls may need a lot of encouragement doing this exercise because they are not used to thinking about themselves in positive terms. You can use each of the different sections of this exercise when you close the group so that each girl can say something concrete and positive about herself.

Giving Verbal Bouquets: The Flower Pot (Handout H-9)

◆ Photocopy a *Flower Pot* for each girl. Glue the flower pots onto pieces of cardboard (or even paper plates) for stiffness.

◆ Draw one stem for each member of the group.

◆ Give each girl enough Post-It Notes so that she has one for each group member.

◆ Have each girl write something that she appreciates about a group member on the Post-It Note. Have her place it on the stem in that person's flower pot.

◆ At the end of the exercise each girl should have feedback flowers from each member of the group.

◆ You can do this exercise all at once, or at the end of each session where girls give flowers to just one or two people. Make sure that they are all not giving flowers to the same person.

Option: Take a group photograph. Make copies for each girl. Glue the photographs onto the body of the flower pot so that they girls become part of their own bouquet.

FEELINGS

Everyone has feelings. Feelings are the emotional and physical ways in which we learn to respond to our own thoughts and to what goes on in the world around us. They provide us with information which helps us to understand ourselves better. Our feelings tell us what we want, what we like, what is safe and what is not, and about our reactions to other people.

From birth we all have the potential to develop a whole range of feelings with different degrees of intensity. As we grow up, the society in which we live and our families teach us to express some feelings and to repress others. They also prescribe the form in which these feelings will be allowed to be expressed. For example, girls and women are encouraged to feel only positive feelings, and then only those feelings which have to do with their relationships with others. Good feelings are compassion, love and empathy. Bad feelings are greed, jealousy, and competition. Disappointment is a difficult feeling, because we are taught that if we are disappointed we probably shouldn't have wanted what we obviously didn't get. Insecurity is also difficult to handle—especially for girls who associate 'the perfect girl' not only with being thin but also with being competent all of the time. While anger and hurt are different sides of the same coin, most of us learn to express the hurt but to repress the anger.

It is important for us to be able to identify the feelings in ourselves and in other people. The more definitive the names we know for feelings the better we can come to understand ourselves and tell other people about ourselves. Knowing the name for a feeling gives us more choices about how we express ourselves and how we will react to situations. It is important for us respect other people's feelings even when they are different from ours. Though we might feel one way about something, we need to know that other people may not perceive things or feel emotions in the same way.

Building a Feeling Vocabulary (Handout H-10)

- Give each girl a copy of *Building a Feeling Vocabulary*. Go over the list and see which of the feelings the girls can identify. Some of the feelings will be easier than others. (You might want to modify the list to suit the age level of the group.)

- Add the slang words that girls use to describe feelings to the list. (e.g. stoked, pumped, choked, etc.)

- Have each girl chose a feeling and use it in a sentence. After every girl has had a turn, go around the group again.

Playing Feeling Charades (Handout H-11)

- Photocopy the handout *Playing Feeling Charades*. Cut out the 'feeling' squares and separate them into three piles according to difficulty.

- Divide the girls into groups of three.

- Have each group select a feeling from the appropriate pile and chose a girl to act it out.

- As one group acts out the feeling, have the other groups serve as the audience and guess the feeling.

45.

- If the actor has difficulty, she can ask members of her group for help. You may help her by reminding her to use her body language as well as her facial expressions.

- If the audience is struggling with the feeling, you can give them hints by asking the actor if the feeling is a good or bad one.

- Once each group has had a turn, another girl is selected from each group to act out a feeling.

- You can make up your own slips from **Handout H-10** *Building a Feeling Vocabulary* if you feel that these are not challenging enough.

Dealing with anger

We spend a lot of time in our groups on *anger*. The taboo against our expressing anger is so strong that most of us don't even realize when we are angry. Because we are raised to be 'nice,' we learn to turn our anger against ourselves and give it a different name. Instead of feeling angry with someone else, we say that we are angry with ourselves. We tell ourselves that we feel fat, ugly, stupid, etc. Sometimes our anger seeps out and we express it indirectly through sarcasm, hostility, or by withdrawing from other people. Sometimes the anger boils over and we attack verbally or physically. Because we have difficulty with our own anger, we can't handle the anger of others. Yet anger can be a gift when it is expressed respectfully—as a way of telling people that you care enough about the relationship between you that you want to set things right. How you deal with anger in your group will depend on your own comfort level and experience.

Recognizing Anger

- All feelings are energy. Anger is a form of energy. Where can you feel it in your body? What happens to energy when you can't let it out? What are some ways that we can let out the angry energy without hurting someone else?

- Sometimes we don't know we are angry. We find out from some of the things that we tell ourselves. What are some of the clues that let you know that you are angry? That other people are angry?

- Sometimes we are angry but don't know how to express it effectively. Let's look at some ways people express their anger badly and why these ways don't work. Let's look at some examples of how people express their anger positively. What are the differences?

- Sometimes we are angry but it is too scary to tell someone directly. How can we tell someone symbolically? (e.g. talking to a chair or to a pillow, or talking out loud without the person being there.)

Holding a *Dead Flower Ceremony*

We often give people live flowers to show our love and appreciation of them. Why not send them dead flowers (symbolically) when we feel angry, hurt or disappointed?! You can use real flowers or make flowers out of tissues or paper.

- Let the girls know that sometimes we get angry with people or are feeling hurt and disappointed—but it's too scary for us to tell them directly how we are feeling. If we keep the feelings inside, they turn into *grungies* so we need to express them. A safe way to do that is to talk to the person symbolically when they are not actually there and can't respond.
- Have the girls think of someone with whom they are angry. If anger is hard for some girls then use words such as annoyed, just a bit upset, etc. Ask them to think about what they would like to say to the person if they were not afraid of hurting them or being hurt themselves.
- Place a garbage can in the center of the room.
- Have each girl stand in front of the garbage can, say out loud what she would like to say to the person and then throw the flower and her feelings into the can. Once she has said what she needs to, she can let the feelings go. If you are doing this exercise with a large group, have the girls write what they want to say on the paper or tissue instead of saying it out loud, and then throw the flower and feelings away.

The girls in a grade 9 group that I facilitated were able to bring real dead flowers because the group was held in June. The ceremony went over so well that the next week each girl came to the group carrying a full bag of dead flowers! The garbage can that day over-flowed with feelings that would otherwise have remained inside.

STRESS

Girls become acquainted with stress at an early age. They see their parents run short of money, lose their jobs, try to juggle childcare and work outside the home, and bring home the effects of stress from the workplace. When jobs or life situations cause families to relocate, or when there is divorce or a death in the family everyone feels the stress of change. It is not only the adults who suffer from stress. Girls have their own stresses to contend with. They have to deal with pressures at school, the ups and downs of friendship, and being bullied and teased. They have to deal with the transition from different levels of school such as from elementary to junior high or high school, family conflicts over taking care of siblings, wanting independence from parents who are afraid to let go, illness, accidents and other physical or emotional situations that have long term effects.

While stress is part of life, it can cause problems when girls don't cope with it effectively. Stress can affect their concentration in school. It can affect their sleep, their appetite, make them anxious or irritable or depressed. It can cause panic attacks, stomachaches, diarrhea, skin problems and tension in their body. Prolonged periods of stress can make them sick.

Identifying Stress

- Ask the girls if they know what *stress* means.
- Ask them to think of one situation where they felt stressed.
- Ask the girls what tells them that they are under stress? What are the symptoms?
- How do they behave?
- How do they feel?
- How does their body react?
- Where do they hold stress in their bodies?

Drawing a Stress Tree

- Give each girl a sheet of drawing paper.
- Have the girls draw a large tree trunk.
- Have the girls think of things, people or situations that cause them to feel stressed.
- Ask them to draw and label a leaf for every one of these situations.
- Divide the girls into groups of three. Have them compare their trees.
- Ask them to make a list of the stresses that they have in common, and a list of the ones that are different.
- Have them share their answers with the larger group.
- Discuss how girls cope with stress.

Relaxation—Breathing Out Your Stress

- Have the girls sit in the chair comfortably with their feet on the floor. (You could also have them lie on the floor).
- Ask the girls to put their hand on their bellies, just below their navel.
- Ask the girls to close their eyes and to begin to breathe. Have them breathe in so that they can feel their bellies going up and down and their hand moving.
- Tell the girls to image the sound of the ocean coming in and going out, or a ribbon of color moving up and down as they breathe.
- Tell the girls that if they have a thought, to let it float away.
- Tell the girls that as they breathe, the stress is going out of their bodies through their fingers and their toes.
- Continue the exercise for a few minutes having the girls breathe out their stress.
- Ask the girls to image a place where they feel relaxed. Stay in that place for a few minutes.
- Tell the girls that when they slowly open their eyes they will remember what it is like to be in that place.

Some girls may have difficulty remaining still for so long, keeping their eyes closed or breathing into their bellies. You might have to encourage the girls to just do what feels comfortable for them and/or adjust this exercise to suit the level of your group.

OUR BODIES

Our bodies are our areas of greatest vulnerability. They are the stage upon which we play out our experiential dramas. When we are confident we walk tall. When we feel depressed or down our shoulders slump. We hold our stress in our bodies so that our backs hurt and our muscles feel tight. Our face turns red when we are angry or embarrassed. It turns white when we are afraid. When we feel that we have very few choices and therefore little or no control of our lives, we try instead to control our bodies through the food that we eat or don't eat. We measure our self-worth and self-value by our physical characteristics, our size and shape. When we don't have the language for self-expression, our bodies become the context and the language of fat becomes the means of expression.

As adults many of us rarely experience our own bodies—especially if we've been sexually or physically abused as children. When we focus on our external image and on how we look, our body no longer feels that it belongs to us anymore. This sense of alienation begins during puberty as men and boys make comments about our developing bodies and especially about our breasts. We become confused by this kind of attention, because it is implied that we are supposed to feel flattered when what we really feel is shame.

The more information that we have about our bodies—how they work, where we store our feelings, the areas where we feel physically strong or weak—the more connected we are to our bodies and therefore the more ownership we feel. For that reason, I have provided information about puberty and growth.

Our growth

Our growth is slow and steady through childhood until we reach adolescence—about 2½ inches, and 6½ to 7½ pounds each year. At nine years of age girls and boys are usually the same height, but girls weigh more. We grow faster during adolescence than at any other time in our lives after infancy. About 20% of our adult height and 50% of our weight are gained between the time that we are 12 until age 18 years. (These ages vary depending on when puberty begins.) Most everything doubles in size: our skeletal mass, heart, lungs, liver, spleen, pancreas, various glands and sexual organs (including the uterus). While our genes determine when puberty begins for us individually and how fast we grow, our sex determines that boys get the shoulders and girls get the hips.

Most girls in North America grow fastest between the ages of 10 to 14 years. They grow an average of 10 inches taller and 40 to 50 pounds heavier. After the age of 14, girls grow more slowly in height and weight—adding weight to all areas of their bodies mainly in the form of fat (especially to the breasts and hips). Fat gain at this time plays a role in regulating the female hormones *estrogen* and *progesterone*, which are necessary for menstruation and pregnancy. The percentage of body weight naturally made up of fat is

1½ to 2 times greater for women than it is for men. Muscle growth in puberty occurs at an earlier age in girls, so this is the one time in our lives that we are naturally stronger than boys.

Puberty and change

Puberty is the time in a girl's life when her body changes from that of a child into that of a woman. These changes happen slowly and gradually, over an extended period of time. They can begin to happen as early as eight years old or as late as sixteen. Girls begin to get pimples, and to grow pubic hair and hair on their legs and under their arms. Their skin begins to produce oils that change not only the texture, but also the smell of their perspiration. Their hips get bigger, their bodies' rounder, and their breasts begin to grow. The area around their nipples (the aureole) becomes a little raised and might even change color. Because not all girls go through puberty at the same time, along with dealing with the changes in their own bodies, many girls must also deal with feeling out of step and different from other girls. Girls who mature early are teased about their breasts and are sexualized. Some begin to date prematurely and become sexually active when they are not ready. Girls who mature later are teased because of their lack of breasts and often believe that there is something wrong with them.

Puberty can be a difficult time for girls. While fat is necessary for sexuality, it is also a dirty word. As girls get bigger and begin to deal with zits and oily hair, they are offered role models that look like boys with breasts. As their hormones begin to rage and they are introduced to PMS; they are encouraged to be passive and placid. No wonder many girls begin to feel out of control as they gain weight and get bigger. With no guarantee of a positive outcome, each day becomes defined by whether or not their jeans fit.

Although menstruation is such a major event in the lives of girls it still remains hidden in our culture. While we want to see ourselves as modern and liberated, we have internalized centuries of societal taboos that view menstruation and the woman who is menstruating as unclean. We have 'the curse,' our 'monthly,' or our 'period.' It's 'that time of the month' for women who are 'on the rag.' Never does the word *blood* pass our lips. Nor is it ever mentioned or shown in the commercials for tampons and sanitary napkins—products that we keep well hidden from view.

Until girls reach puberty, most girls feel unselfconscious about their bodies. They run and jump and are physically active. They are able to accommodate themselves to the changes that occur as they grow because these changes are so gradual that their bodies continue to feel the same. When girls enter puberty, however, they go through so many changes so quickly that their bodies feel new and strange to them. Most girls feel their bodies are abnormal and that they are the only ones that have the fears that they do.

What Girls Want to Know about Puberty

? I noticed that I have started to grow in my chest. Does this have anything to do with my period?

? How will I know when it will come and will it hurt?

? What happens if I get it in the middle of class?

? The first time I got my period the blood didn't look like real blood. Does that mean that there is something wrong with me?

? If I don't get my period each month, does that mean that I am not normal?

? What does anemia mean? Am I going to get anemia?

? How come they never say how bad cramps can be during your period?

? What is a yeast infection?

? What is a swab wipe or pap smear?

? What is virginity?

? Why do girls go into puberty before boys?

? How old do you have to be to get your period?

? I haven't started menstruating yet but I have gunk in my panties. Is this normal?

? Why do I gain weight at that time of the month?

? What is the oldest age to normally have your period?

? Is it true that girls of 9 and 10 are maturing?

? Why do girls get nervous when they get their periods?

? Why do girls get hormones?

? What about zits?

? My breasts hurt sometimes. Does this mean that I have cancer?

? Do girls' breasts have to be fully developed before they get their periods?

? How fast does pubic hair grow?

? Do I have to gain weight during puberty?

Unless puberty education is prohibited by the schools or organizations sponsoring our groups, we need to be able to provide girls with a safe place where they can ask the questions that are of real concern to them. This doesn't mean that we have to be experts. When we can't answer a question, we can tell the girls that we will look it up. When I was gathering information about puberty I was amazed at how much I didn't know—and how much I then learned.

When we just give girls information and ask them if they understand, they rarely ask the questions that make them feel vulnerable or embarrassed but are of greatest concern. Initiating an open discussion about puberty means creating a safe environment, giving girls permission, naming their fears and diffusing the taboos that we place on talking about our bodies and about menstruation.

Talking With Girls About Puberty

- Acknowledge their discomfort with the subject: I tell girls that puberty can sometimes be difficult and that even though it can be hard to talk about it, we need to know everything we can about our bodies—because these are the only bodies we are ever going to get.

- Normalize their fears: I tell them that no two girls go through puberty at the same time and in the same way. Everyone sometimes feels that they are not normal and are the only ones who feel that way.

- Talk about what it is like to be a late bloomer and an early bloomer. It's hard to be the only girl in grade five who has breasts or the only girl in grade nine who doesn't have them. Talk about the stresses involved and about how the stage of development that girls are in affects how they perceive and relate to their bodies.

- Defuse subjects that are taboo: I ask girls if they ever noticed how sometimes we make a big fuss over a guy who is growing a mustache for the first time, but are embarrassed about our periods when we get them. I ask how many of them would come into class announcing 'I got my period, I got my period.' (Laughter helps break the tension). I ask them where their mothers keep their tampons and what would happen if someone like Sarah McLachlan opened her purse on stage and a tampon fell out.

- Provide them with anonymity: I ask girls to write their questions on index cards and to put the cards into a basket. I tell them that I will be as honest as possible even if I am feeling uncomfortable. And if I can't answer the question, I'll look it up and answer next week.

- Suggest books that they can read. Girls are starving for information about themselves. While my book *When Girls Feel Fat* was originally intended for parents, it is girls from 11 years old and up that seem to be reading it first in any household.

Body image/awareness

Body image is a term that describes how we see our bodies. It is the mental picture that includes our thoughts, feelings, judgments, sensations, and awareness of our body. Our body image is shaped by what we tell ourselves about our bodies, how we feel about our bodies and what messages we receive from other people. For example, many women who are fat often have a positive kinesthetic experience of their body's softness and of their sensuality. However, these women may have a negative body image because the societal messages that they receive tell them that fat is bad. Our body image is also influenced by illness, disability, puberty, pregnancy and menopause.

Because girls are encouraged from birth to value themselves in terms of how they look, their body image is connected to (and often forms the only basis for) their self-esteem. In the same way that girls begin to lose their self-esteem during adolescence, they also begin to lose the holistic, healthy awareness of their bodies that they had as children. As their bodies begin to change during puberty, girls disregard the internal experience of their bodies and focus solely on how they look to others. In our groups we help girls redirect this external focus to an internal one by providing them with alternative ways of visualizing, conceptualizing and experiencing their bodies.

Tracing Our Body History

Have girls bring in family pictures. Talk about body history—about their genetic, racial and ethnic make up and who girls resemble in their families. Look at how many different family members live in our bodies.

My Body Type

- Bodies come in three distinct types:
  Endomorphs tend to have rounder body types, with more body fat and softer curves.
  Ectomorphs are slim, less curvy, more angular.
  Mesomorphs are muscular, with wide shoulders and slim hips.
- What type are you? If it is too early to tell, then what type is your mother, your father?
- Different body types do better at different physical activities. What kind of physical activities make you feel good?
- What kinds of activities make you feel awkward?

Taking Care of Our Bodies

By the time girls reach adolescence they have learned that taking care of their body means 'looking good.' What other ways do we need to take care of our bodies—rest, sleep, good food, and protection from physical harm, etc.?

Saying Yes and No

This exercise allows girls to use their bodies to express their feelings.
- On the count of three have girls clench their fists and jump up. As they come down have them shout 'No!' as loud as they can. Repeat two more times.
- On the count of three have girls jump up as high as they can and reach for the ceiling. As they come down, have them shout, 'Yes!' as loud as they can. Repeat two more times.
- As them which is easier for them—the *yes* or the *no*.
- You can discuss why it is hard for some girls to say no and for others to say yes.

(Girls love this exercise. The amount of female energy in the room is really powerful.)

Developing Body Awareness

Tell the girls that how we hold our bodies can influence how we feel as well. Ask the girls to walk around the room as if they are depressed, as if they won the lottery, in a 'masculine' way, in a 'feminine' way. How does their awareness of their body change each time? Ask girls to think of situations when they felt really small. Did that make them feel powerless? What else were they feeling? Ask them to stand up tall and imagine that situation. How do they feel? Ask them when they felt really big. What else were they feeling? Did they feel that they took up too much space? What does taking too much space mean? How did that feel?

Drawing Our Bodies

Part 1: Using rolls of brown or white heavy paper, have girls draw an outline of each other's body. Have girls use different color felt pens or crayons to color in these different parts:

*   Those parts that they use a lot.
*   Those parts that they really like.
*   Those body parts that are the strongest, those that are the weakest.
*   Those parts that they have confidence in—that work when they want them to.
*   Those parts that give them pain.
*   Those parts that make them feel embarassed.

Part 2. Have girls walk around as if they were the only person in the room. Walk as if:

*   They were feeling angry. Where would they feel anger in their bodies?
*   They were feeling sad. Where would they feel sadness in their bodies?
*   They were feeling hurt. Where would they feel hurt in their bodies?
*   They were feeling disappointed. Where would they feel disappointment in their bodies?
*   Using different colored felt pens, ask the girls to color in those places in their bodies where they feel those feelings. Before you do each one, have the girls imagine what it felt like when they walked around the room. Ask them to imagine a situation where they felt the feeling. If they don't know where the feeling is in their bodies, have them guess. Remind the girls that there is no right or wrong to this activity.

(You might have to do this activity over two sessions. You can do Part 1 or Part 2, or do both.)

How I Feel about My Body (Handout H-12)

♦ Divide the group up into pairs or into groups of three.

♦ Have each girl do her own *Body Attitude Inventory*. (Remind them that they cannot fail.)

♦ Have the girls discuss their answers in small groups.

♦ Have them share their answers for questions 1-6 in the large group.

♦ Talk about how putting your body down is another *grungie*.

Worrying about weight

It's impossible to grow up female without ever 'feeling fat' and worrying about weight. From the time that they are young, girls receive very clear messages from their family, friends, boys and the media that not only do they have to be attractive—but attractive means being thin. Girls are constantly bombarded with the message that they can change their bodies if they try, and that there is something wrong with them if they are not trying hard enough.

Girls are not only pressured to be thin, but also to fulfill the attributes attached to thinness. The models that girls are led to emulate are one-dimensional, so girls never see the realities of these women's lives. What they interpret from the constantly smiling faces and lack of affect is that they, too, should appear perfect—which to them means always being confident and in control like they imagine the models to be. This is opposite their accumulated experiences during adolescence—with its emotional ups and downs, frequent mood changes, and with the self-consciousness that comes with the belief that all people are looking at you all of the time. Girls who are feeling out of control are not only offered an unrealistic picture of what they should look like, but also an unattainable image of how they should behave.

Adolescent girls channel an enormous amount of their energy away from their own feelings and experiences into worrying about how they look, what other people think of them and into feeling fat. As they compete with each other over who is thinner and who eats the least, they reinforce a culture of thinness amongst themselves.

What Girls Want to Know about Feeling Fat

? Why are girls so ashamed about their bodies—like hiding their bodies under loose big shirts and pants?

? Why don't girls accept themselves for who they are?

? What is the average weight for a 13-year-old? For a 14, 15, 16, 17 year old?

? Is it true that stripes going down make you look thinner?

? You say that 'feeling fat' is just a cover for a deeper feeling but what if we don't think there is a deeper feeling? The only deeper feeling I personally see is self-consciousness. Do you consider that a deeper feeling? Why?

? When I sit in class sometimes I feel self-conscious about whether or not my thighs are flattened out or whether my sides are sticking out. What should I do?

? How can I convince myself that I am fine the way I am? I know that I don't have to change for people to like me, but I just can't think of my physical appearance without finding fault.

? What do you recommend for someone who is lonely and feels fat? Everyone makes plans for Friday or Saturday night and no one asks me along.

? Why do girls see fat when there isn't any?

? Why is it that whenever my boyfriend puts his arm around my waist I feel fat?

? How do you help yourself? My concern for my body image controls my thoughts daily, hourly… and so on.

? Why do I feel so insecure about my weight even in front of my friends who are girls?

? If you ask someone if you are fat and they say no, how do you know if they are lying or not?

Most of the questions that girls ask can be answered by reminding them about the *grungies* and helping them understand what lies underneath their fear of fat and their need to appear thin. Every time that a girl panics because of the size of her thighs or worries about how she looks or feels fat what she is really saying is 'I don't like my body,' which really means 'I don't like myself,' which in turn means 'I'm not sure what I'm really feeling and if I was I couldn't express it anyway.' This is learned behavior. Underneath every *grungie* there is **always** a story waiting to be told.

As well as helping girls deal with their own *grungies*, we need to teach them the skills to deal with others. Girls often engage in a self-defeating ritual. One girl says, 'I feel fat.' The second one says, 'No, you're not.' 'Yes, I am,' replies the first girl. 'No, you're not,' says her friend. After a while the first girl feels frustrated because she's trying to say something but it's in code and so it is not acknowledged. Her friend feels frustrated because there isn't anywhere for her to go in this exchange. Instead of feeling the intimacy that comes from communication, both girls feel distant and unheard. By teaching girls to help each other decode the language of fat we help them not only reconnect with their selves but also with each other.

Empowering girls who *are* fat

A group of teenage girls were asked on a TV program if they would rather be a rich fat person with a fabulous career or someone who is thin, poor and unemployed. They all looked at the interviewer with horror that she would even suggest there was a choice. Fat has become the 'f' word of our time, the dirty word. We count fat by grams—like pharmacists measuring prescriptions. We trim it from our budgets and pride ourselves on our deprivation. It's hard for us to see it as having any positive value, or to acknowledge that we might die if we were to get rid of it totally. No matter how much we talk about acceptance of individuality, in our heart-of-hearts the one thing we don't want to accept is fat.

Fatism or weight prejudice is one of our society's remaining socially accepted forms of prejudice and discrimination. While it may no longer be all right to make comments about someone's race, religion, gender or sexual orientation, it is acceptable to make hurtful comments about their weight. Often people justify their behavior by self-righteously expressing fear about the health of people who are fat. Yet the link between health and weight continues to be tenuous. Fat phobia has little to do with something as rational as health. It has more to do with how we feel about ourselves. The harder it is for us to accept our own bodies, the more the fat person represents our greatest fear.

It's difficult for a fat girl to develop self-esteem and to feel loved and accepted when the society around her finds her size—and therefore the girl herself— unacceptable. When we as adults try to help girls to lose weight in order to fit in, we negate who they are right now. When we try to protect girls from hurt by ignoring their fat, we pretend that something that is a major issue in their lives doesn't exist. When we tell girls that it's what's inside that counts and encourage them to focus on their personalities, we reinforce the myth that you cannot be beautiful and fat. Fat girls internalize our messages as well as the ones that they receive from society as a whole. Their low self-esteem is often caused not so much by being fat, but by the shame that they feel being despised by a culture that only values people who are thin.

As facilitators, we need to help fat girls be fat with dignity. We need to listen to their feelings about being different without trying to fix it or minimize their feelings or try to make them feel better. We need to let the girls in our group know that it is normal for them to come in all sizes and shapes and to acknowledge the differences in girls, including those who are fat. We need to bring in pictures of girls and women of a whole range of body sizes and talk about them in terms other than of how they look. We need to encourage fat girls to use their bodies so that they can be proud of their strength. We need to diffuse the value judgments around fat by using the word in the same way that we would use the words for other characteristics such as thin, tall, curly hair, straight hair, blue eyes, etc. We need to let our fat girls know that it is all right for them to be who they are.

Physical activity and sport

Girls begin at an early age to underestimate and undervalue their capacity for physical activity. By the age of six, girls and boys believe that boys are simply better than girls. By grade four, girls begin to show deference to the boys in mixed team sports and physical education classes and exhibit a reticence to put themselves forward.

When girls reach the end of grade seven their aerobic fitness level begins to decline. As girls go through puberty they become self-conscious about the physical changes in their bodies and will avoid any sport or activity that exposes them to physical scrutiny. Because of ineffectual physical education programs, allocation of resources to boys, lack of parental encouragement, or cultural and societal prohibitions against strenuous physical activity, many girls do not have the opportunities to develop the necessary motor skills. They do not learn to perform basic bodily movements with confidence and many have not had the chance to develop skills such as throwing, catching and hitting. Even when girls are given the opportunity they won't participate when their skill level is low.

It is important for girls to use their bodies when they are young and to continue to be physically active as they go through adolescence. Just 30 minutes of physical activity a day can increase peak bone mass in early adulthood, reduce the risk of coronary heart disease and breast cancer in adulthood, and delay the onset of osteoporosis. Girls who are physically active are found to be healthier, less susceptible to stress, more independent and have greater self-esteem. They are more at ease with and accepting of their bodies. They are more likely to delay their first experience of intercourse and, later on, more likely to practice safe sex. They are also less likely to smoke.

We need to advocate in our schools and recreation centers for girl-only gym time, and for a wider range of physical activities that interest girls and that are geared towards different body types. We can join organizations such as Promotion Plus, a non-profit organization in British Columbia which works to ensure gender equity in sports and physical activity for girls and women. We can support women coaches who reinforce the socializing and friendship aspects of girls' sports instead of focusing solely on winning and losing. We can encourage girls to use their bodies, explore their fears and hesitations with them, and direct them to programs appropriate to their age and skill level. One such program is *On the Move* which targets adolescent girls who are reluctant to participate in sports and physical activities (see RESOURCES). Where resources are available, we can add a physical component to *JUST FOR GIRLS* groups. Girls are equally as successful as boys in physical fitness and ability when they are encouraged to participate in physical activity that is relevant to their gender, when they have active female role models, and are raised in a school system that provides same-sex developmentally appropriate activities based on skill, body awareness, cooperation and minimum aggression.

Encouraging Girls to be Physically Active

♦ Use photographs and illustrations of models of realistic weight (and overweight).

♦ Focus on the activity rather than the shape of the model herself.

♦ Allow girls to choose their own clothing.

♦ Focus lessons on enjoyment, participation and skill development.

♦ Emphasize the fun aspect and the benefits of social interaction.

♦ Be a role model—emphasize that you enjoy the benefits of being physically active.

♦ Debunk the myths of sweating and injuries.

♦ Ensure that girls receive the same amount of time, resource allocation, equipment and instruction that boys do.

♦ Partner with your community center—share facilities and staff.

♦ Offer female-only gym time. Don't give up if attendance is low to begin with.

♦ Provide female role models of athletes.

♦ Acknowledge different skill levels.

♦ Provide activities where everyone can do well.

♦ Provide childcare for teen moms.

♦ Encourage diversity—pay attention to who is not there and encourage them to attend.

OUR RELATIONSHIP WITH FOOD

Most of us women grow up with an uneasy relationship with food and eating. We learn to categorize what we eat into foods that we really *want* but can't have, foods we *should have* but don't want, foods we think are *healthy*, and foods we think will make us *fat*. As women, we are supposed to cook, but we're not supposed to eat—at least not in public. We're not supposed to have appetites. Eating with gusto and without apology is sometimes seen as aggressive or unfeminine behavior. We serve others first and never question that we get the leftovers, or the broken piece of pie. Most of us don't know when we're hungry or when we are full. Because our knowledge of nutrition comes mainly from counting calories or grams of fat, we rarely think of fueling our bodies to make ourselves strong.

What we eat and how we select food is influenced by many different factors. Sometimes we eat for psychological reasons as a way of dealing with feelings that are difficult to express. Food is an important part of our social life. Many of us are born into cultures that are identified by unique customs that focus on food. Our eating habits are influenced by the availability of food, by how much money we have or don't have, and by our individual tastes.

While our unresolved relationships with food do not in themselves create eating disorders, they can develop into disordered eating and can strengthen our preoccupation with food and weight. Girls internalize society's attitudes towards food. Their erratic relationship to food often begins in grade six when they skip breakfast. Girls sometimes skip breakfast because there is no food in the house, nobody home to prepare it, or to talk to while they are eating. Some girls are responsible for younger children (either their siblings or their neighbor's children) and have no time to eat themselves. One of the consequences of not eating is being constantly tired and feeling 'spaced out.' This means not being able to concentrate in class.

Girls need to eat more during puberty because they are growing, but they often see their need to eat as abnormal (as do we) and restrict their food intake because they are afraid of gaining weight. During adolescence girls constantly juggle their need for 'junk' food as a way of establishing independence and their choice of 'healthy' foods as a way of remaining connected to their families and not getting fat. Often they take in too much fat and too little iron, calcium and zinc. In our groups we help girls normalize their relationship with food by giving them good nutritional information and helping them look at why they select different foods and what these foods mean to them. We encourage girls to eat a variety of foods including those which they label 'junk' and 'healthy.' We also help them make the connection that feeling 'spaced out' has little to do with being 'stupid' and everything to do with a lack of nourishment. Respecting your body means giving it sufficient fuel—not allowing it to run on empty.

What Girls Want to Know about Food

? I eat and eat and think that I am not normal. My mother says that I am going through a growth spurt. Is that true?

? What can we do so that we don't lose control with the food we eat?

? How much food should I eat?

? My mother is always saying I never eat enough but she's not with me all day or after school. I'm 15. Shouldn't I be responsible for myself? I eat non-stop.

? If you aren't hungry at breakfast, do you eat or not?

? If you are picking at your food and someone thinks you're a pig and tells everyone, how do you stay out of the 'everyone is going to hate me' state?

? How come even if we don't like how we look and how our body makes us feel, we can't turn down a single donut?

? Do you have to eat vegetables every day?

? Does eating 'junk' food make your boobs bigger?

? If a person wants to eat and eat how do you stop yourself?

The Food You Eat

- What is your favorite food?
- What is your least favorite?
- Who does the cooking in your house?
- Who decides what you are going to eat?
- Describe a favorite eating experience.
  Where were you?
  What did you eat?
  What did the food taste, smell, feel like?
- Describe the perfect meal.
  Where would it take place?
  Who would be there?

Exploring Your Eating Habits (Handout H-13)

Sometimes the foods we chose and the reasons why we chose them are similar to those of our friends, sometimes different. We also have times when certain feelings make us want to eat certain things. Go through the range of feelings on the sheet. Ask the girls if they have any others to add.

Explore the Myths around 'Good' Foods and 'Bad' Foods

- Make lists of the foods that are considered 'good' foods and 'bad' foods.
- What makes these foods 'good' or 'bad'?
- How nutritious are they?
- How do you feel when you eat them?

DIETING

Most of us have been on diets. We usually go on one during the stressful periods in our lives. If we feel that we can't control what goes on around us, then we try to control our food. Girls practice the same behaviors that we do. It is estimated that at any given time 61% of adolescent girls and young women are on a diet and that girls as young as five are restricting their food intake because they are afraid of getting fat. Yet no matter how much we diet, we can't really change our basic shape. And even though we might feel good when we initially lose weight, the reality is that we have a 95% chance of gaining it back within the next two years.

'Set point' theory suggests that diets do not work as we suppose and can, in fact, make us fat! The 'set point' theory holds that everyone has a genetically determined weight range that our body attempts to maintain. When you diet, your body cannot tell the difference between a deliberately constructed low-calorie diet and an actual famine. Once you reduce your caloric intake, your body seeks to protect itself from starvation by gradually burning fewer and fewer calories, making weight-loss ineffective. When you go off the diet, your body will work not only to regain the weight that you have lost, but also to store extra in the event that you will try to starve it again. The *set point* is thus raised to a higher natural weight range and we eventually gain additional poundage.

Some people believe that people are fat because they eat too much. They think that fat people should diet because it is unhealthy to be fat. Both of these beliefs are false! Overweight people often eat the same or sometimes lesser amounts than people who are thin. Eating is only one factor that affects our weight. Others include our genetic makeup, our personal metabolism, and the amount of activity that we do which burns calories. While people who are regarded as overweight are known to be at risk for heart disease and diabetes, yo-yo dieting leaves us vulnerable to these very same risks. In children and adolescents, dieting may interfere with normal growth and development. Dieting is often the first step on the road to developing an eating disorder.

Another myth is that it is easy to gain weight and that thin people, by the very nature of their thinness, are naturally healthy. These beliefs are also false. In the same way that your metabolism (or the rate at which you burn calories) can make it hard for you to lose weight, it can also make it hard for you to gain. It takes an adolescent girl approximately 3200 calories per day to gain two pounds in a week. And while 'thin may be in,' the highest mortality rates are for women who are underweight.

Exploring the Myths about Dieting (Handout H-14)

Have girls answer the True or False questions in the handout and discuss their answers. Answers:

1 – False	4 – False	7 – False	10– True	13 – True
2 – True	5 – False	8 – True	11 – False	14 - True
3 – False	6 - False	9 - True	12 - False	

What *Really* Happens When We Diet (Handout H-15)

This handout provides you and the girls with practical information about dieting.

BUILDING COMMUNICATION SKILLS

Communication involves sending and receiving messages in such a way that both participants can understand them. During a conversation we switch back and forth between being the sender and being the receiver as we take turns talking and listening. While we usually communicate through words, we also communicate in non-verbal ways through our tone of voice, our facial expressions, gestures and the way that we hold our bodies.

Good communication means that we can talk and listen to each other in such a way that we understand what it is like to stand in the other person's shoes. We don't have to agree with her or do what she wants when she wants it. It means that we understand how things are from her perspective. Good communication opens the door for negotiation. It leaves us feeling connected to each other even though we might disagree.

Good communication means taking responsibility for ourselves. This means using 'I' in our sentences instead of always pointing the finger and saying 'You.' It means verifying our perceptions instead of assuming that we know what the other person is thinking or what they heard.

Assertive behavior

Being assertive means being clear and direct about what we want and what we think while at the same time respecting the rights of others. We use assertive behavior to stick up for our rights, to let people know what we want and to let them know what we will or will not do.

Do:	**Do Not:**
◆ State your opinions and feelings.	◆ Blame the other person.
◆ Use descriptive terms.	◆ Use 'You' messages.
◆ Use 'I' messages.	◆ Interrupt.
◆ Explain why.	

Example: You are at the crucial point in a mystery book and your mother keeps interrupting you:

Non-Assertive Communication: 'Stop bugging me!' 'You always interrupt me when I'm reading.'

Assertive Communication: 'I would like to finish this chapter because I'm at the exciting part and then I will talk to you.'

Making Assertive Statements (Handout H-16)

- Talk about what being assertive means. Give examples of assertive statements. Ask girls for their own examples.

- Divide the girls into groups of three. Have each group fill out the handout.

- Have the groups demonstrate the statements to the larger group.

Responding Assertively to Situations (Handout H-17)

- Cut out the scenarios in the handout. (You can change them to ones that are more appropriate for your group.)

- Divide the girls into groups of three. Have each group act out a different scenario.

- After each performance, encourage the audience to offer suggestions as to how they would have handled the situation.

Giving feedback

Giving people feedback means letting them know how their behavior affects us. We want to get the message across in such a way that the other person will listen and not feel blamed or criticized.

Do:
- Describe the behavior. The aim is to give the other person a clear idea of what she did that made you react.
- Be specific. Talk about just the one incident.
- Describe the feelings that you had.
- Use 'I' statements
- Describe the outcome or effect that this behavior had on you.

Do not:
- Blame the other person.
- Use statements such as 'You always…'

Example: Your friend keeps borrowing your clothes. She promises to return them the next day but that never happens. She usually keeps them for two weeks.

Bad Communication: 'You're so unreliable. You never give my clothes back.'
'Other people have been saying that I shouldn't lend my clothes to you.'

Good Communication: 'When you borrow my clothes and don't give them back right away (*Describes the Behavior*), it bothers me (*Describes the Feeling*) because I can't wear the clothes that I want (*Describes the Effect*).'

Dealing with the response

Good communication means giving the other person a chance to respond. Because that person is different from us, they may not see things in the same way that we do. Their first reaction may be a feeling of being blamed or criticized, or they may feel hurt or angry by what we say. We need to remember that everyone comes equipped with his or her own unique set of feelings. They need to take in what we say, think about it and then react. Good communication doesn't mean taking feelings away from the other person or retracting our own feelings in order to make them feel better. It means letting the other person know that we understand how they can feel they way that they do even if our reality is different and we don't agree.

Do:

- Listen with curiosity. Try not to plan your response in advance.
- Ask yourself if there are any parts to her story or to her response where you can see how she might have felt the way that she did.
- Acknowledge her feelings. Let her know that you can see how she feels the way that she does. You might not have felt the same way, but you can respect how she feels.
- Use 'I' statements.
- Tell your side of the story and ask her if she can see how you felt as you did.

Do not:

- Blame or get into a competition over who is right. This is not a contest.

Example: You have told your friend how you feel when she borrows your clothes. At first she feels hurt that you don't trust her. She also feels criticized. Then she tells you that it's not her fault. She didn't return your clothes right away because her parents were fighting at night and she was too tired in the morning to remember about your clothes.

Bad Communication: 'You said you would return my clothes the next day, so it's your responsibility.' 'It is your fault!'

Good Communication: 'I'm not trying to hurt you or criticize you by what I'm saying. I just want you to know how I felt. I can see how it must be hard for you with your parents. Can you see how I feel about my clothes?'

Dealing with defensiveness

Sometimes when we practice good communication, the other person has difficulty hearing us because she feels criticized and therefore *defensive*. People who are defensive often respond with 'Yes, but...' They also try to vindicate themselves by turning the blame on us. They say things such as 'Well you always...' or 'When you...' If we respond to what they are saying then we get caught up in a spiral that takes us away from our original statement and away from what we want them to hear.

Do:

- Keep your message simple.
- Describe the behavior and how you feel.
- Let the other person know that you are not criticizing her.
- Be patient, keep repeating your message over and over again until she hears you.

Don't:

- Respond to her defense.
- Blame her.

Example: You have told your friend how you feel when she doesn't return your clothes on time. Your friend feels criticized and responds by telling you that you didn't return her CDs when your borrowed them.

Bad Communication: 'Yes I did. I gave them back to you last Saturday. You're the one who is unreliable.'

Good Communication: 'I'm not trying to criticize you. But when you borrow my clothes and tell me that you will return them right away, it bothers me when you don't—because when I want to wear them, they are not there.'

Telling Someone How Their Behavior Makes You Feel (Handout H-18)

- Divide into groups of three.
- Cut apart the scenarios in the handout and hand them out separately to the different groups.
- Have each group act out a different scenario.
- After each performance, encourage the audience to talk about how they would have handled the situation.

Dealing with conflict

It's impossible to have a relationship with someone without ever running into conflict. No matter how much we love someone or think that we understand them, there will be times when we have differences. We may want different things, or have different perspectives on situations, or we may have made assumptions about the other person that are wrong, or we've said things (perhaps unintentionally) that has caused the other person to feel hurt or angry. Conflict can be scary, but it also can be healthy. When we resolve it successfully—by having each person feel heard—we feel closer to the other person, not further away as we may fear.

Rules for Good Communication and for Fighting Fairly (Handout H-19)

Conflict Role-playing:

We encourage the girls to role-play their conflicts with their friends. This gives them the chance to practice different ways of communicating, and of trying out new behavior in a supportive environment.

- Divide the group into threes. Have the girls think of a conflict that they are having at the moment or that they have had recently.
- Have each group select one girl who has a conflict, one girl to play her friend and the third girl to monitor the situation.
- Go over the *Rules for Good Communication* (H-19) and the sections here on *How to Give Feedback* and *Dealing with the Response*.
- Have the girls role-play the conflict. Have the third girl stop them each time they break the rules.

66.

- If there is time, switch the roles or repeat this activity on another day.
- At the end of the activity, ask the girls what the experiences of role-playing and monitoring was like for each of them.

FAMILIES

It's difficult to be a parent of a girl today. The girls in our groups come from all kinds of families. These include two parent families with one parent at home (usually the mother), two parent families with both parents working, single-mother families, single-father families, blended families, and same-sex families. While these families are different in form, most are dealing with the same issues—too little time, too little money, and too much guilt. In many cases, the girls end up being secondary caretakers—not only reinforcing the nurturing role, but also learning to sacrifice their own needs to satisfy the needs of others.

Most mothers want something 'better' for their daughters—no matter how good their relationships with their own mothers. In order to help their daughters make an easier adaptation, many mothers try to help them to 'fit in.' Mothers bring factors concerning their own socialization into their interactions with their daughters and often inadvertently reinforce society's biases. Women who have not been taught to recognize and value their own developmental processes can't validate them for their daughters. The messages that girls get are mixed and conflicted—have a career, and/or have a husband, and/or have children and... be thin.

The myth that we must separate during adolescence in order to gain independence in order to grow up, means that most women (seeking to mother 'correctly') disconnect from their daughters at a time when neither they nor their daughters really want that to happen. This leaves girls feeling unsupported and abandoned.

At the same time that girls experience a rift in their relationships with their mothers, their relationships with their fathers are in danger of breaking down. Because of the cultural differences between women and men, many girls interpret their fathers' male use of language either as criticism or as a demand of high expectation—even if that is not the original intent. Men, in general, deal with fear by attempting to control the situation; so many fathers express their concerns about potential risks to their daughters by attempting to control their behavior. These dynamics are exacerbated by the difficulty that many men have in dealing with their daughters' emerging sexuality. Because boys are socialized to close down their feelings at an early age, many men grow up with unmet emotional needs. They learn to feel close and connected to women through sex. As their daughters mature sexually, they find it difficult to maintain the emotional closeness that they might have had when she was growing up—a closeness that was built upon androgynous camaraderie. As a result, they either distance themselves emotionally from their daughters or become overly dependent upon them and make them into secondary mothers or wives.

Families are extremely important to adolescent girls. Even though they may act as if they want them to disappear, their families provide them with the emotional base from which they can engage with the world. When girls in early adolescence talk about their families, their concerns center on lack of privacy, having to take care of siblings, and not being heard. In middle adolescence girls talk more about their need for independence and the pressures on them to achieve. Some girls complain that their mothers don't care enough about their feelings and activities. Other girls complain that their mothers care too much—and wish that they would get a life of their own! Girls talk about wanting to be more a part of their fathers' lives and about their pain over the distance that they experience. Some girls talk about the use of alcohol in their families, of constant fighting and of too little money.

When girls bring up issues around their families, we validate their experiences and try to help them find ways to express their feelings and opinions to their parents in a manner that will encourage their parents to be responsive and supportive. This means being very specific about issues and trying over and over again to achieve good communications. We also help girls develop coping skills so that they can deal with situations that are outside their control.

All Kinds of Families (Handout H-20)

- Tell the girls that children come from all kinds of families.
- Go over the handout and ask them to identify the kind of family that they come from.
- Ask them if they know other families that look like some of these examples.
- Even if families are different in structure, what do they have in common?

Bricks and Bouquets

- What are the things that aggravate you about different members of your family?
- What are the things that you appreciate about members of your family?
- What would you need to say to them to let them know how you feel?

Family Tree

- Draw your family tree: How far back can you go?
- If you are adopted, how are you grafted onto your family tree?
- Who are you the most like? Why?
- Who would you like to be like? Why?

Draw Your Family

Using stick figures, draw your family. Draw everybody in terms of who is closest to whom.

- Who are you closest to?
- Who are you furthest away from? Why?
- If each person could tell you one thing about themselves, what would it be?
- If you had a chance to say something to each person without their becoming angry or hurt, what would it be?
- If you could change your family, what would it look like?

Your Family's Values

Our values are the things that guide us through life, and influence how we interact with the world. Some of the values that most families maintain are similar. Others are different. Often the values that girls adopt or try out during adolescence may seem different from those of their families.

- Talk about what values mean and the different values that we have in common.
- Have girls divide a sheet of drawing paper in two. Have them put the title *My Family's Values* on one side of the paper and list those values.
- Have them put the title *My Values* on the other side and have them list the values.
- Ask girls to circle the values in both columns that are the same.
- Divide a flip chart into the same columns. Have girls fill in both sides.
- Talk about the conflicts that arise when the values are different. Point out that these conflicts are not the same for all girls.

FRIENDSHIPS

Girls grow up in *relationship* to other people. The strength and integrity of these connections help them define their sense of self and provide them with a sense of well being. In childhood, girls have confidence in what they know and think and feel. They are extremely sensitive to (and very verbal about) unfair and uncaring treatment. Think about all of the girls that you know that are passionate about animal rights, for instance. Girls trust in their abilities to express and resolve differences between themselves. They are able to speak their minds directly—because they do not fear that what they say might contribute to the end of relationships as they know and experience them.

As girls move into adolescence, they begin to reinvent themselves in order to adapt to the dominant male culture. They come to label their energy, vitality, desires and thoughts as bad or wrong or selfish. By so doing, they lose the ability to hold on to the truth of their own experiences—especially in the face of conflict. They begin to see themselves as others imagine them, and begin to reframe their thinking (and thus themselves) to fit this definition.

During adolescence, the quality of the relationships that girls have with other girls begins to change. While the need for connection remains the same, the rules become distorted. Remember how it was when we were in grade 5 or 6 or 7? We had our 'best friend' and we were inseparable. We shared our deepest secrets and promised that we would be friends forever. Then we went to school, and had to deal with other girls. Each class or grade had a gang or crowd or clique with a 'popular' girl as leader, her follower (or followers), and their victims. Although the girls who filled the different roles changed from time to time, the roles themselves remained the same. The games we played with each other were based on exclusion and some were very painful. There was always one girl who was designated the victim because she was the smartest, the prettiest, the ugliest, the dumbest, the most sexually developed, or for any other reason. She was cast out, ostracized by the group. The rest of us would give anything not to be excluded—even if this meant betraying or being betrayed by our best friend.

When we entered junior high or high school we struggled with the very same issue that still concerns us as adults today: how can I be friends with you and still be true to me? We held back our feelings because we were so afraid of hurting the other person and losing the relationship—even if that relationship was one we really didn't want. Because we didn't have the skills necessary to deal with conflict, we either blamed the other person or distanced ourselves from her—both strategies guaranteed to cause a rift in the relationship and drive us further apart. Even though we listened to our friends and tried to understand them, we were convinced that no one would ever understand us.

As adolescents we obsessed for hours about our friendships. Because we were not able to be honest with one another, we often felt insecure. Even though we knew what qualities we appreciated in our friends, we had difficulty recognizing those same qualities in ourselves or believing that the other person would value things about us that they didn't see in themselves. We listed all the things we weren't and wanted to be, and held that up as a standard for ourselves.

What Girls Want to Know about Friendships

? Why do girls exclude other girls when we know this just hurts each other?

? If your friend is mad at you and you have said you're sorry and she doesn't forgive you, do you think she hates you because you have gained weight?

? Why do friends have to be so mean?

? Why do people use their friends to make them look good and the friend look bad?

? Why do I always feel that other girls hate me?

? Friends should be trusted but if you go to a presentation on something kind of embarrassing, they shouldn't laugh. They should stand beside your opinions. Right?

? What can I do to improve a weak friendship?

? Do you think that we should say how we feel or keep the rude comments to ourselves?

? How do you say no to someone without hurting her feelings?

? How can you say your feelings without hurting someone?

? What do I do about someone that I tried to be friends with but it's hopeless?

? What should I do with my anger when I don't like someone?

Helping and over-helping our friends

Taking care of others (or helping them) is a wonderful part of who we are. But sometimes we become so engrossed in the other person's experiences and feelings that we neglect our own. We become so concerned with them that we forget where the other person ends and we begin. Recognizing that each of us is a separate person with our own feelings and experiences, and separating our experiences and feelings from those of our friend's is called a *boundary*.

Sometimes our boundaries get blurred. When that happens we end up feeling powerless or resentful or even angry. This happens when we want to help someone but our helping them creates a conflict between their needs and ours. Their problem may be too big or too much for us but we don't know how to say no—because we don't want to let our friend down. Sometimes we feel scared that we won't do the right thing, or we feel resentful because our friends are asking too much. Sometimes we try to get it over with by telling our friends what to do. When they don't do what we tell them to do, we feel angry and they feel pressured and misunderstood.

One of the areas where girls want to help their friends is around eating disorders. Girls want to be there for their friends and feel powerless that they can't help their friends change the behaviors or convince their friends to get help. Girls need to know that the best thing that they can do is be supportive and voice their concern. They can't help their friends by monitoring the behaviors nor can they make their friends get help if their friends don't think that anything is wrong. Girls need to know that their best course of action is to speak to an adult who can take charge—even if that makes them feel that they are betraying their friend.

Girls love to talk about relationships. In fact, they'll do this to the exclusion of everything else. Yet don't we all—it's our interest in people's lives that keep all those talk shows flourishing on TV. In our group discussions, we attempt to redirect the girls' focus back onto themselves. This means getting them to recognize and articulate their own responses to others, as well as validating those skills, which they use to support and empower one another. We use role-play and discussion to talk about helping and over-helping, about boundaries and about saying 'no.' We examine how these situations lead to *grungies* and try out different ways in which they can be resolved. We also teach communication skills.

71.

Best Friends (Handout H-21)

It is important to focus on qualities and not on 'good' things and 'bad' things. We let the girls know that the qualities that bug one person may attract another.

- What's the best part of having a best friend? What is the hardest part?
- Who is your best friend? How did you meet and become friends?
- What are the similarities between you? What are the differences?
- What interests do you share? What are the things that you disagree about?
- What are three qualities that drew you to her? What are three things that bug you?
- What do you think are the qualities in you that draw her to you? And bug her?
- What are some of the problems that you have with your friend?
- How do you resolve them?

What I Want in a Friend

- Have girls divide a piece of paper or drawing paper into two sections.
- In the first section, have girls list the qualities that they want or value in a friend.
- In the second section, have girls list the qualities that they think they should have in order to be a good friend.
- Have girls put a check mark next to the qualities in Section 1 that they think they have.
- Have girls put an x next to the qualities in Section 2 that they don't have.
- On a flip chart list the qualities that girls think make a good friend. Then list the qualities that they think they should have. Center your discussion on how hard it is for us to value the things in ourselves that we value in others or to imagine that we have qualities that the other person feels she doesn't have. Remind them that when they think they should be a certain way, they are guaranteed to feel insecure because they have discounted themselves.

Telephone Twins

If you would like to encourage interaction among the girls outside the group, then set up a system of telephone twins:

- Write the name and telephone number of each girl on the sticky side of a post-it note.
- Draw a telephone pole on a piece of cardboard.
- Stick the post-it notes on the pole so that the empty side is facing you and the name and telephone numbers are hidden.
- Tell the girls that at the end of the session they are going to pick a twin from the pole.
- Each girl telephones her twin once a week.
- After three or four weeks, create another telephone pole and have the girls pick a new twin.

CHOOSING A PARTNER

In my work with women I often ask them how they came to be in a relationship with the person that they are with. Nine times out of ten the answer is, 'That person was interested in me.' As adult women, we put more effort into researching a used car than we do in choosing a partner, at least with the car we kick the tires! With the partner, we sometimes end up being kicked—physically or emotionally. We're so busy pleasing the other person so we won't be rejected that we forget to ask ourselves if that person is really someone that we want to be with in the first place. In exchanging 'me' for 'we' we never actually look at who the other person is—at the qualities that we are drawn to, as well as those that make us want to pull away.

As girls enter the world of heterosexual relationships their behavior is very much like our own. Girls are either chosen by boys or choose boys that other girls have labeled 'cool.' Often there are no other criteria. Girls then expect the boys to relate to them in the way that their girl friends do. When boys don't talk to them, can't schmooze with them nor share the details of their lives, girls don't recognize that their discomfort is because of gender differences. They think that they have done something wrong—if only they were prettier, skinnier, blonder, etc. *then* the relationship would be a success.

Girls have different attitudes towards sex than boys do and experience their sexuality differently. Most boys have their first sexual experience early in adolescence. It usually occurs through masturbation. They experience sexual satisfaction that has little to do with intimacy. The first time that adolescent boys have intercourse the same separation between sex and intimacy occurs. Adolescent boys learn that they are players in the game of sexuality. They are studs. Each time they score validates their masculinity.

A girl's first heterosexual encounter is usually with a boy that she feels close to. The first time that she has intercourse it is with someone with whom she is in love. Despite the career choices offered to women today and the numbers of single families around them (often their own), adolescent girls still envision themselves getting married, having children and living happily ever after. Often girls feel hurt when they are confronted with the gender differences around sexuality—when they have 'love' with a boy who has 'sex.' Girls also have to deal with the double standard that judges as *sluts* girls who plan in advance to have sex, or have sex with more than one person.

Girls focus on their partners to the exclusion of their own sense of reality and sometimes their personal safety. Because their primary concern so often is pleasing the other person in order to be loved, many girls have difficulty recognizing or extracting themselves from relationships that become abusive—or saying *no* when they don't want to have sex. Even if they know about safe sex, they will risk pregnancy, HIV/AIDs, and other sexually transmitted diseases rather than displease their boyfriends by insisting that they wear a condom.

73.

When I talk to girls about guys (their favorite topic) I always mention that not all girls are interested in boys. Some girls are not clear about their sexual orientation during adolescence. Some girls are attracted to other girls. I tell them that when we make the assumption that every girl is interested in guys, it makes it difficult for girls who are not to acknowledge or talk about what they are experiencing. It also makes them feel that they are abnormal and that they are the only ones who feel this way. I also try to monitor my language and choose words that are more neutral. I try to use the word partner instead of boyfriend, for example, because it is more inclusive.

In our groups we help girls take the focus off the potential partner and bring it back to themselves. We encourage them to become the choosers rather than be the choosees. We take the emphasis off romance and make the other person real. We do this by helping girls recognize the qualities that draw them to the people they are interested in, as well as the qualities that make them want to move away. We help girls recognize when relationships are abusive and give them the skills with which to say no.

In some groups the facilitators talk about sexuality. Whether sexuality is a topic that you wish to address will depend upon your level of comfort and the mandate of your group. In some school districts, talking about sex is a definite no-no. If you do talk to the girls about sex, it is important that you put your values and attitudes aside and help them explore theirs—so that the choices that they make are healthy ones.

What Girls Want to Know about Boyfriends

? Why is it that when you like a guy and you finally get him, you feel you're not good enough for him and then you start to do things that make you look better and then you realize that you don't look better?

? Why is it that when you are going out with a boy other boys think you are pretty—but if you are not then they think you are ugly?

? Should you have sex with guys to feel loved?

? I really feel bad when a very hot guy is going out with an ugly girl. Everyone thinks I'm pretty but when that happens my self-esteem drops. What should I do?

? Does the age difference matter if you are interested in a guy a lot older than you are?

? How do you address your problems with guys?

? How do you deal with rejection?

? Is it wrong to yearn for affection?

? I have a friend who is a girl and I want to spend all my time with her. Does this mean that I'm a lesbian?

? Why do guys only go for skinny girls?

? If you like a guy but are nervous when you look at him, how do you start a conversation with him?

? Should I tell the guy I like that I like him or hold my feelings back?

? How do you get past feeling fat so that you feel like a sexual person?

? How do you know when you've come too far to say no to a guy?

Choosing a Partner (Handout H-22)

Describe the following about a person that you are interested in: appearance, personality, likes or dislikes:

◆ What kind of person is this person?

◆ How are you alike and how are you different?

Describe the ideal partner:

◆ How would that person make you feel?

◆ How would you interact with one another?

◆ What kinds of things would you do together?

◆ How would you want that person to treat you?

◆ How do you expect that person to make you feel?

◆ How would you want that person to be with your friends?

Consider These Questions Early in a Relationship (Handout H-23)

Sometimes girls get into relationships with boys who are abusive. There are many reasons why they don't leave. Some girls believe that this is the way that boys are supposed to be, and they have no other choice if they want to have a boyfriend. Some girls are afraid to hurt the boy's feelings even if he is abusive. Some girls believe that if the boy is abusive it must be their fault. It is very important to spend time on this handout—especially with girls who are in middle adolescence.

SCHOOL

Along with parents and the media, the school has a powerful influence on reinforcing gender attitudes and socialization and, therefore, on how girls feel about themselves. Girls receive conflicting messages. They are told that they can be anything they want to be—yet they may not have the role models, the societal support, or the self-confidence to realize their aspirations. Unlike boys (who are likely to name their talents as something that they like about themselves), too many girls see self-worth solely in terms of physical appearance. They learn to attribute their successes to luck and their failures to their own inadequacy. They begin to feel that they are not good enough or smart enough to achieve their dreams.

Despite the best of intentions, many schools still teach a 'hidden curriculum' which reinforces gender roles and attitudes. Just at that point when girls are making the transition from girlhood to womanhood this curriculum instructs them that boys remain the central focus in every aspect of this culture. Schools do this in the following ways:

- The curriculum and learning materials still don't show girls and women in realistic ways, nor do they include the full range of human experiences.
- The language that is used in the classroom is often sexist and affects what is taught and how it is taught.
- Boys dominate interaction in the classroom. Teachers interact differently with boys and girls, and expect different levels of achievement from them—shortchanging the girls.
- Sexual harassment is still common even in elementary schools, and girls fear for their safety on playgrounds, in hallways and in classrooms. Girls experience a range of gender insults and verbal put-downs during their educational endeavors from male students and occasionally from teachers as well.

The stories that the girls tell in our groups are consistent with these findings. The girls describe the ways that they are treated differently in class. Teachers call on the boys more often, and enforce different standards of conduct—the girls feel that they get punished for behavior that is overlooked in the boys. Girls are grouped with boys against their wishes so that they can be used to settle the boys down. In gym, teachers spend more time on male-dominated team sports than on activities (such as gymnastics) that are requested by the girls. When teams are picked, girls are chosen last and given the least important positions. Boys pass the ball to them only under duress. When girls complain, they are mocked. As well as experiencing sexism, elementary school girls have to deal with harassment. They speak of male teachers who make comments about their developing bodies and boys who point at and try to touch their breasts.

In our groups we validate the girls' experiences and name them. We let them know that studies have been done to show that the inequality they are experiencing is common. We talk about the ways that girls learn and help them identify the kinds of teaching that make them feel confident or make them feel stupid. We talk about sexism and harassment and let them know why these situations occur. It is important that sexism and harassment be named and described in order for girls to feel that there is nothing wrong with them as people—they are not to blame and are not responsible for triggering behavior that makes others act in inappropriate ways. We role-play and discuss strategies around how they can express their feelings and change or stop the behavior. We look at the support available to them in terms of their mothers and friends should they feel safe enough, or want to talk to, the school authorities.

Gender equity

As group facilitators we can help girls name and describe their experiences, help them express their feelings, and teach them skills to help them feel more included in school. As teachers we can practice gender equity in our classrooms. As women we can work within the system and from outside to insure that gender equity is practiced in our local schools.

Promoting Gender Equity

◆ When you ask questions in class, wait a few seconds to give the girls a chance to respond.

◆ Give girls feedback that describes their skills, behaviors and activities and not their looks or how 'nice' they are.

◆ Pay attention to group dynamics—who speaks, how often, for how long, in what order and who interrupts whom. Since girls tend to speak less often and for shorter periods of time, be sure to acknowledge their contributions.

◆ Make students aware of gender dynamics in participation. Have different students record the interactions.

◆ Expect equally high performance from girls and boys. Ask them both the same kinds of questions.

◆ Create girl-only times on the computer. Girls feel safer if they don't have to compete with boys for space and resources.

◆ Vary your teaching methods. Have students do some of their work in small groups. Remember that the presence of one boy changes the dynamic of a group and be careful not to assign the one girl the task of quieting the boys down.

◆ Encourage modeling and coaching among students. Girls learn best in a cooperative setting using concrete 'hands on' activities.

◆ Show women and girls in leadership roles, rather than just as helpers or victims. Show boys and men being emotionally vulnerable.

◆ Hang pictures or posters that show men and women involved in a range of activities inside and outside the home.

◆ Create girl-only times in the gym and encourage girls to participate in sports and physical activity. Even if girls don't participate at first, with enough encouragement they will come.

MEDIA

In a workshop that I conducted for Big Sisters Organization, I asked the Big and Little Sisters present to describe the perfect girl or woman. Because the group was racially and culturally mixed and ranged in age from 11 to 40 years old, I thought that they would come up with several different descriptions. In fact, there was only one. The perfect girl or woman is Caucasian and is tall, thin, and blonde and has big lips and big breasts. She is 'nice' and caring. She never loses her temper, has zits or PMS, or is angry or insecure. We've integrated the Barbie concept so profoundly into our collective psyche that there is no room for any other model—even among black, Asian and Hispanic girls.

Girls in adolescence project themselves psychologically into a world that is populated by perfect girls and women. Even girls and women of color are portrayed by the media in ways that exhibit the narrow range of socially approved 'white bread' characteristics. Women who are fat, old, handicapped, wear glasses, are pregnant or represent ethnic minorities are rarely seen as major players. They are only occasionally represented in 'character' parts.

The media not only creates an image of how girls and women should look but also defines how they should be. In the 1998 sitcoms on American television women are personified as adorable dopes. While they may have been smart and spunky in their teens and early twenties by the time they reach their thirties they are, perennially confused, perpetually underemployed and adorably confounded by men. These messages are deadly to adolescent girls who are fighting for their voices and for their selves. Gone are older women such as *Murphy Brown, Cybill,* and *Roseanne* who raged with self-confidence and irony.

When people don't see themselves reflected in the popular culture, they don't question that there is something wrong with the culture—they begin to think that there is something wrong with themselves. And without experience to the contrary, we tend to agree with them. In this way, whether it is deliberate or by default, the media plays an influential role in reinforcing stereotypes that determine how we define ourselves. This also fuels the dynamics of racism and sexism that we inflict upon one another.

While the media cannot be said to cause eating disorders, it contributes by perpetuating a preoccupation with food and weight that robs us of our sense of self and leaves us powerless to change society's emphasis on 'thin is in.' By showing only thin women in major roles, by portraying women who are constantly watching their weight, who never eat a decent meal or eat with gusto and by targeting female audiences with commercials for diet regimes, the media perpetuates the myth that everyone should be thin and can be thin if only they try hard enough. It lends a cloak of reality to what is false. It idealizes a female shape that is statistically unusual. It communicates to girls who are going through puberty that their bodies are unacceptable or deformed to be growing this way.

Magazines for women reiterate these same messages. They constantly encourage women to try the latest diet and, at the same time, provide recipes so that they can cook real food for somebody else! These magazines promote unrealistic eating behavior by displaying photographs depicting plates with very little food on them as normal. The woman trying to lose weight is reassured by such manipulation that she has eaten quite enough—and has no need or right to still feel hungry.

The images, texts and practices selected for use by the media encourage girls and women to be overly concerned with their appearance (and all their advertisers' products) and less concerned with the values and conduct of their lives. By its depiction of, and by tacitly condoning, such a narrow range of social acceptability and behavior, the media's messages make girls vulnerable to the many social and health risks that are triggered by insecurity. In our groups we fight back by helping girls decipher these messages from the media, and by providing them with a wider range of choices then those that are being presented to them.

Counteracting the Messages of the Media

Bring in magazines:

◆ Make a collage of the different ways in which women are portrayed.

◆ Make a collage of the 'ideal' woman depicted.

◆ Make a collage of 'realistic' women.
   Who gets included in each collage?
   Who gets excluded?
   Where do you fit in?
   Who are the women that you admire?
   What are the things that some of these women do in their daily lives?

◆ Look at pictures of models. Gather information about the technology involved in making someone appear this way.

◆ Look at the magazines at your local supermarket.
   Count the number of magazines that have diets on the covers.
   Count the number of magazines that tell you how to take care of somebody else.

Becoming Media Literate (Handout H-24)

Talk about how we need to become media literate in order to be able to understand the real messages that the media displays.

Divide the girls into three groups:

◆ Talk about the TV shows that they like to watch.

◆ Have each group watch a different show during the next week or two.

◆ Have each girl fill out her form and bring it back to the group.

◆ Have each group present their findings to the larger group.

◆ You can modify this activity to address advertisements as well.

BULLYING

At a grade seven workshop that I was facilitating I asked for volunteers to role-play how to deal with teasing and bullying. I chose 'shoes' as a topic that would be neutral enough so that the girls playing victims would not end up feeling personally hurt by the bullies. In each role-playing situation, the girls who were the 'bullies' demonstrated the exquisite cruelty that girls (and boys) inflict upon one another. They curled their lips and sneered. Their voices were contemptuous and taunting, their body language menacing. It took tremendous effort and support for the 'victims' to not collapse. Even I felt like running from the classroom to go and buy a more stylish and acceptable pair of shoes!

Bullying occurs when one person or group is repeatedly hurtful and harmful to another. It is one of the most frequent and difficult situations that students have to deal with in school today. An incident of bullying takes place once every seven minutes and lasts about thirty-seven seconds. Its emotional effects can last a much longer time for the victim—and for others who witness the bullying. Its physical effects can be deadly.

Bullies tend to be more aggressive as they grow older. Half of first-graders who are disruptive, unable to get along with other kids, disobedient with their parents, and resistant with teachers will become delinquents in their teen years. By the time that they are 24 years old, 60% of bullies have a criminal conviction. Sexual harassment that begins in elementary school escalates in high school into date rape and, at its most extreme, into adult ritual domestic violence.

Bullying does not happen because of miscommunication between two people. Bullies seek power. Their intention is to put the victim in distress. Boys bully other boys and bully girls in order to elevate their own status and increase their sense of adequacy. Girls bully girls who they see as a threat to their relationships with other girls and to their relationships with boyfriends. There are different kinds of bullying. While both girls and boys engage in each of the different kinds of bullying behavior, they tend to focus on ones that are congruent with their gender culture and development.

Physical Bullying is usually done by boys—although this is a growing problem among girls. They kick and hit the victim and/or take and damage the victim's property. They become more aggressive as they get older.

Verbal Bullying usually takes the form of teasing and name-calling in order to hurt and humiliate others. Bullies emphasize whatever makes the victim different from his or her peers. They use insults and racist comments. When girls tease each other their aggression focuses on body size and personal characteristics. The worst thing they can call one another is 'fat.' When boys tease each other their verbal aggression often takes the form of homophobic and misogynist comments such as 'fag,' 'wuss' and 'girl.'

Relational Bullying is most often done by girls who exclude other girls from their peer groups, spread nasty rumors about them, tell secrets about them, tease them and frame them and set them up for punishment. This kind of bullying is devastating to girls who are rejected from their peer groups at the time that they need them the most.

Sexual Harassment is also a form of bullying. In elementary school girls are called 'sluts,' 'whores' (or 'hos'), 'cunts' and 'bitches' by boys who pinch their breasts and lift their skirts. In many high schools girls can't walk down the halls without being grabbed and groped. Girls who beat up other girls (whom they label as sluts and who they see as threats to their boyfriends) are also practicing a form of sexual harassment.

Dealing with bullying is difficult. Because we adults don't know what to do, we often hide behind creative denial. We tell the boys to fight back and the girls to walk away. We tell girls and boys to stop being so sensitive. We normalize teasing by telling them that this is what they have to expect from life. We talk about zero tolerance in our schools but we don't enforce it. This teaches students that no one will stand up for them. As a result, they often don't report these incidents. They feel embarrassed and humiliated, are afraid to be seen as 'squealers' and fear retribution that is ten times worse than the original bullying.

Students who are being bullied often become reluctant to come to school, or to walk there and back all alone. They have headaches, stomachaches and other bodily symptoms. They show signs of depression such as low energy, difficulty in sleeping, and eating too much or too little. They don't want to talk about what's happening in school and if they do, they don't want parental or teacher intervention because they are afraid of being singled out and being made subject to worse treatment. This sometimes leads to suicide.

Students can't stop bullying on their own. In order to put an end to bullying, teachers, students, support staff, administration and the community must work together. Adults must provide students with safety if they inform on the perpetrators. This means guaranteeing students that the bullying will stop; that it will be stopped in such a way that no one knows who reported it, and that the bully will be treated firmly but with understanding. If the adults don't follow up with action, then the students will feel not only unsafe but also betrayed.

In our groups we encourage the schools to take a stand. We recognize that although we as individuals acting alone cannot stop bullying behavior, in the context of a group program we can help girls build friendship connections and therefore reduce the isolation that makes them vulnerable. We also help girls name the behavior, validate their feelings, ensure them that they have a right to safety, and teach them skills and techniques for dealing with bullying situations.

Talk about Bullying

- Invite girls to talk about bullying. Let them know that bullying is hurtful and that they have the right to be safe when they come to school.
- Encourage details: What do people call you? What do they do? Talking about bullying in a safe atmosphere helps validate the individual, lets her know that she is not alone and helps her get rid of the shame.
- Describe bullying as an issue of power. Girls need to know that it has nothing to do with their adequacy or inadequacy as a friend or how they look.

- Describe bullying as a school and community problem. Talk about who needs to be involved in order to stop it.
- Explore who can help, who is safe and who is not.
- Encourage girls to be safe by participating in the group, joining activities and finding someone to stick together with.

Fighting Back: Role-Playing Situations and Solutions

Divide the group into threes:

- Have one person from each group chose a time when they were bullied.
- Have the group act out the scenario.
- Encourage the person who was bullied to change the ending to one that gives her a sense of power.

'Stop! I don't like what you are saying!'

- Bullies usually stop if we don't react to the content of what they are saying. Our reaction is what fuels their aggression. Review the section on *Defensive Behavior*.
- Chose two volunteers—a 'bully' and a 'victim.'
- Each time the bully says something, have the victim repeat: 'Stop, I don't like what you are saying.' 'Stop, I don't like what you are saying.' (It's tempting to respond to the content, so the victim may need additional support.)
- Divide the group into threes. Have two girls practice together. The third girl is the coach.

'Stop! She doesn't like what you are saying!'

Sometimes it is difficult for girls to stand up to someone all alone. They need an ally.

Divide the group into threes:

- Have one girl be the bully, one girl the victim and the third girl the supportive friend.
- Have the supportive friend repeat to the bully over and over: 'Stop! She doesn't like what you are saying!' 'Stop! She doesn't like what you are saying!'

Violence and aggression

While boys tend to be more outwardly aggressive than girls, we need to remember that girls are also aggressive—especially adolescent girls whose emotions are strong and whose impulses are hard to control. Without the skills to recognize and deal with intense feelings in constructive ways, girls and boys may direct their aggression in ways that are harmful to themselves and to others. Because girls are socialized to internalize their distress and because direct aggression in girls is frowned upon, many girls deal with their aggression towards each other indirectly. Where boys fight, girls talk. Girls ten and eleven years old have already developed a lethal set of social and verbal skills. They become relational bullies. In the past few years more and more girls have begun to externalize their anger in the same way as boys and use physical aggression against one another. Because female violence is a growing social problem, I've included it here so that you can understand the dynamics that lie underneath.

According to Sibylle Artz, a sociologist at the University of Victoria in British Columbia, many different factors contribute to female violence. These include family dysfunction, sexual and physical abuse, neglect, sexual inequality in and outside of the home, and the constant exposure to violent and misogynist messages that girls receive from the culture. Girls (and boys) are bombarded with images in rock music and videos that reinforce the message that women are not as good as men and that women are only worthwhile as sex objects.

In her study of violent girls, Artz found that many grow up in families that are characterized by problems with alcohol misuse, marital discord and family violence. Girls learn that men are far more important and powerful than women. Men are stronger and more forceful. This gives them the right to make and uphold rigid rules that they enforce through physical and emotional punishment. They push, punch, humiliate and blame. They hold the person who breaks these rules responsible for making them angry and frustrated. This allows them to believe that her punishment is justified. Girls who experience this kind of behavior replicate it outside their families.

Girls who experience violence at home continuously act out both parts of this dynamic in their relationships with others. Because they identify with the underdog, they fight to protect smaller or younger girls who are being picked on by girls who are older and bigger than they are. At the same time they will beat up these same girls who are beneath them in the social order when they image that these girls are being disrespectful to them. Like their violent parents, girls feel that their behavior is justified because they are meting out punishment that fits a specific crime. And like their parents do at home, girls shift the responsibility onto the victim whom they see as the cause of their anger.

Most of the violent acts that girls engage in are a result of competing for boys. Most of these girls have experienced sexually abusive messages, sexual harassment or other abusive behavior and are afraid of being sexually assaulted and being forced to have sex against their will. However, because boys are central to their definition of self-worth and because they have internalized the misogynist messages of their culture, girls normalize this behavior as a 'natural' part of being male. They see it as being caused by hormones and physical urges beyond the control of the boys. Because these girls ascribe to a double standard around sex, they also enforce a rigid code that says girls who experiment sexually or initiate sex are sluts and deserve to be punished.

Girls who are violent live in a world where their female culture is almost totally negated. Their connection with their mother is quite weak. Their friendships are tenuous and are often based on alliances against other girls who are seen as competition for boys. Because many of these girls have been sexually abused, their level of trust in relationships is very low. Often these girls grow up with feelings of low self-worth. They drink and smoke more than non-violent girls, lie and stay out all night, damage their parent's property and act up more often in school if they experience disrespect from the teacher. They often feel fat because they, too, ascribe to the societal ideal of thinness and have no way of expressing their feelings or talking about what is real. Being disconnected from other girls and from most of the people in their lives, they have no place in which to feel heard, validated, respected or to feel that they count.

As facilitators we need to understand and to help girls understand what this violence means to them. We also need to address it in the context of their lives. By helping girls reconnect with one another and reclaim their female culture, we can help them develop and strengthen their sense of self—so that they can learn other ways of handling situations. At the same time, we need to ensure that any girls in our group who are violent have professional individual counseling so that they can deal with their issues around anger and around sexual and physical abuse.

JUST FOR BOYS

It's not that easy to grow up as a boy today. Boys are more likely than girls to have learning disabilities, to be put into special education classes and to drop out of school. More and more boys are being diagnosed with Attention Deficit Disorder (ADD) and Attention Deficit Hyperactive Disorder (ADHD) and are on behavior modifying medication. Since 1990, prescriptions for Ritalin have increased 500% in Canada. Boys make up the majority of people with schizophrenia and the majority of retarded children. Emotionally disturbed boys outnumber girls four to one. Rates of depression in boys are increasing, as are disordered eating, eating disorders and the use of body enhancing supplements such as steroids. Boys are twice as likely as girls to be victims of physical abuse, three times as likely to be the victim of a violent crime and four times as likely to commit suicide. They are also more likely than girls to use drugs and alcohol, to deal with situations through violence and to end up in jail.

If we are going to help boys grow up to be healthy, to feel good about themselves and avoid the social and health risks they are vulnerable to, then we need to understand what it means to be male in today's society. We need to understand how boys develop, the uniqueness of their male gender culture, and the social pressures that they face as they grow up and enter the adult world. We also need to develop programs for them that honor who they are and not what we want them to be.

The factors that determine male behavior

From conception boys and girls are programmed to march to different drummers. As the section on CULTURE illustrated, boys have different perceptions, priorities, behaviors and skills because of the influence of different hormones and structural and functional differences in their brain. They also process and act upon information differently. For example, boys are more task-oriented than girls are because the male brain turns on in order to carry out tasks and turns off once they are completed. Their attention span and motor activity are also shorter in duration but are made up of more active periods and are quicker in frequency. These traits make boys better suited to activities that include quick bursts of energy rather than sitting still for long stretches at a time. While boys have better spatial relations than girls do and are better able to deal with the abstract, they take in less sensory stimulation. They smell less well, taste less well and get less input (and less soothing) from tactile information. They hear better in one ear than the other and often hear less well, which sometimes gives the impression that they are not listening. Because their brain processes track quickly from object to object in three-dimensional space they do well in activities such as computer games, but they have difficulty maintaining eye contact with others. Boys receive more testosterone (and less of the neurotransmitter seratonin which inhibits aggressive behavior) so they are more action-oriented. They tend to be more aggressive and impulsive and engage in more risk-taking than girls.

Popular psychological theories describe male development as hierarchical, goal oriented and individualistic. According to these theories, boys develop their male identity through experiences of separation and through autonomy—which is measured by individual accomplishment and by how well boys perform in the world. In order for boys to become self-reliant (to learn to stand on their own two feet), they must separate from their mothers at an early age.

Gender socialization begins at conception as parents envision their future sons according to the societal image of masculinity. It attempts to mold boys into men who are aggressive, independent, brave, rational rather than subjective, active, ambitious, competitive, logical, strong in body and mind, and unemotional or able to hide their emotions.

GROWING UP MALE

As infants, boys are more emotionally expressive, more sensitive and cry more easily than girls. For the first eighteen months of their lives they identify with their mother and internalize her basic qualities. Until the ages of three and four, boys have access to the full range of human emotions and to all of the behaviors that we associate with being male and female. They kiss their parents openly and cuddle with them. They cry when they are upset, show their feelings of hurt and distress, look forward to bedtime stories and express their fear of the dark.

Kindergarten–entering the male world

When boys begin kindergarten they enter into the male world where they will be schooled and evaluated according to male measures of success and achievement. Psychologist William Pollack writes that kindergarten marks a crisis point in boys' development that is similar to the one that girls experience in adolescence. Boys are bombarded with messages from the media, from other mothers and fathers, teachers and religious institutions that in order to develop a healthy male identity they must distance themselves from the emotional nurturing relationships they have with their mothers and with anything that has to do with being female. Over and over society affirms the myth that mothers can emasculate their male children by being too close to them and that only a man can lead a boy into manhood. While girls may proudly wear tee shirts that proclaim that they are 'Daddy's Girl,' society labels the 'Mama's Boys' sissies. They are seen as soft, weak, dependent, homebound and emotional. Underlying the cultural message 'Don't make a girl out of him!' is the profound fear that if boys are allowed to be like girls they will end up becoming homosexual.

From the first day of kindergarten boys are expected to measure up to the other boys, to show that they are 'real' boys and that real boys don't cry. Society prepares boys to become men by 'toughening them up' and disciplining them through the use of shame. Boys are expected to close down the relational half of their emotional range. They become ashamed of these feelings—especially those of vulnerability and need. Many boys react to these profound changes in their lives with symptoms such as separation anxiety, bedwetting and loss of their self-esteem as they learn to repress their vulnerability and present only the persona that adults wish to see.

Elementary school–ready or not

When boys enter elementary school they move into a world that is out of synch with their cognitive and physical development. Boys are expected to sit quietly and suppress their natural impulsiveness and need for physical activity. They are required to focus their attention for longer periods than they are capable of doing and to learn by listening even though they do not hear as well as girls do. As they try to adapt to an environment that they are not biologically suited to, boys are presented with learning situations for which they may not be developmentally ready. Many boys develop language skills and fine motor skills later than girls do. As a result, they are not ready to read and write at the time when the primary school curriculum requires them to do so.

Boys who fall behind and cannot succeed in the classroom embark upon a cycle of failure and of shame. The 'good' quiet boys internalize their frustration and distress. The 'bad' boys act out frequently and become disruptive. They are seen as troublemakers and are often labeled as having conduct disorders. Sometimes they are diagnosed as hyperactive. Boys who rarely feel successful in the classroom run a high risk of eventually dropping out of school.

Adolescence–reinforcing the code of masculinity

According to William Pollack, boys undergo a second crisis in their emotional development during adolescence when they experience immense societal pressure to conform to a rigid ideal of masculinity. They repress any overt feelings that they might still have toward their mothers and any characteristics that might in any way be seen as 'female'—because their fathers, their peers and other adults are uncomfortable with them. Boys are rewarded for showing their action-oriented side, for demonstrating physical prowess and for repressing all of their feelings except anger and rage. In order to feel worthy of membership into the community of men, boys learn to detach from their own experiences and to ignore fear and pain. Boys who are 'cool' act tough, hide their empathy and laugh and brush it off when they feel hurt. They tell themselves that everything is just fine, that they can handle anything and convince themselves that they are invincible. They keep their sense of inadequacy and their needs bottled up inside.

Adolescent boys enforce the code of masculinity on one another through a culture of cruelty. Those boys who don't measure up are bullied by their peers and are called *fag*, *wuss* and *girl*. Because most boys feel insecure about and are afraid of losing their own place in the circle of masculinity, they participate in oppression or remain silent about it. This eventually costs boys their capacity for compassion for others and also for themselves.

The code of masculinity prevents boys who are going through puberty from sharing their fears and concerns over their changing bodies and the numerous hormonal surges that they experience. Even when boys fear that the changes in their bodies are not normal (especially the wet dreams) they often feel that they have no one who can understand what's happening to them. They feel insecure about whether they will ever be worthy enough to become a man. They are afraid that they will never attract a member of the opposite sex and that their attractions to members of their own sex means that they are gay. Because few fathers are involved in the every day aspects of child rearing, boys enter puberty with very little experience of intimacy or knowledge of sexuality. With only the culture to guide them in their decisions about sex, boys who long for closeness often become sexual adventurers instead.

During adolescence boys complete the process of disconnection from themselves. They split into two selves in the same way that girls do. The inner self contains the feelings that society teaches boys are unacceptable—feelings such as insecurity, inadequacy, fear, loneliness and need. The outer self reflects an image of male toughness and emotional detachment, which our society perceives as strength. While girls hide their feelings of anger, insecurity, competence and competitiveness behind a persona of 'kind and nice,' boys hide their feelings of shame, inadequacy and fear behind a mask of bravado. As boys lose touch with themselves, the inner self becomes buried and the mask is the only sense of self that they know. Because the price for violating the societal image of masculinity is humiliation and shame, boys will endure emotional and physical pain, take risks and even engage in violence in order to prove themselves and win the approval of their peers.

HOW BOYS DEAL WITH DISTRESS

Most boys are socialized to externalize their distress. They react to situations by considering themselves unfairly treated by others and transform their feelings into anger and blame that they direct against the source. Boys who are highly impulsive and easily frustrated are at risk of inflicting their distress onto others in the form of violence. They do not do well in school. They usually come from families where they experience or witness violence or where their parents alternate neglect and disinterest with random and harsh punishment. Boys may also discharge their distress through the use of alcohol, drugs and through risk taking action-oriented behavior.

Many boys internalize their distress. Their depression often goes undetected by professionals and by boys themselves because boys are socialized not to show their pain and shamed into not complaining. Sometimes the only way that we know that something is wrong with them is when they get into trouble with alcohol or drugs or try to commit suicide. Although more girls attempt suicide than boys, boys are often more successful. Boys can also manifest depression differently than girls do. Psychologist Terrence Real says that addictions and depression are variants of the same disorder.

Disordered eating and eating disorders

While disordered eating and eating disorders are commonly associated with girls, boys are affected as well. Boys make up 50% of compulsive eaters. Boys who are fat are judged as weak and out of control and are shamed and teased by their peers. Before puberty, girls and boys develop anorexia in equal numbers. Once boys reach puberty these numbers decline. Boys reach puberty 2 years later than girls. Their increased muscle, facial hair and deeper voices are valued in our society and thus protect boys physiologically against developing a negative body image. Boys appear to be more satisfied with their bodies and perceive their bodies with less distortion than girls do. When they develop eating disorders they tend to do so in fewer numbers and usually much later on (when they are between the ages of 18–26 years old).

Boys who develop anorexia and bulimia tend to have issues similar to those of girls. These include perfectionistic attitudes, family backgrounds that include rigid rules and high expectations, genetic disposition, parents who are preoccupied with weight, and lack of autonomy. During adolescence, boys who are homosexual may use bulimia as a way of dealing with their gender-orientation conflict and with society's attitudes towards their sexuality.

While the media does not create eating disorders, it has a strong influence on boys who are disposed towards them. Media images of men reflect more male muscle and rippled chests than ever before. The bare male torso sexualizes men and sends a message to boys that their self-worth not only depends on how well they perform but also on how they look. The ideal man with his hard and muscular body, bulging pectoral and taut abdominal muscles, physically reinforces the code of masculinity: tough, hard, unemotional. Some boys and men who feel thin, awkward and inadequate try to bulk up in order to gain an illusion of control in their lives. They exercise and become obsessed with their bodies. They begin to diet and develop anorexia and bulimia in the same way that girls do.

Steroids

About 83,000 young Canadians between the ages of 11 and 18 use anabolic steroids. Most of these are boys around 14 years and older and men who want to improve their performance in sports and/or who want to change the way that they look. Like boys who are at risk for eating disorders, boys who use steroids attempt to gain control of their lives by controlling their bodies. They associate the well-built muscular body with fame, respect, power and sex appeal.

Anabolic steroids are a synthetic version of testosterone, the male sex hormone responsible for the growth of long bones and muscles and for masculine features such as facial hair and a deeper voice. They increase muscle size and help to increase strength by giving muscles the potential to grow stronger and bigger more quickly. Steroids are strong prescription drugs with specific medical purposes. They are also available illegally in the same way as mind-altering substances such as cocaine and heroine. Handout H-25 describes the warning signs and what may happen when boys use steroids.

UNDERSTANDING MALE CULTURE

Boys grow up in a totally different gender culture than girls do with their own language, a different perspective, and different ways of nterpreting and responding to ithe world. Male gender culture forms the basis for what boys consider important, their patterns of communication, the stories that they tell and how they tell them, how they get things done, how they process and deal with their feelings, and how they negotiate their relationships with one another.

Boys have tremendous energy and exuberance, a willingness to venture into the unknown and a need to test their limits and to take action. They are more physical than girls and have a greater need for space. Because male development is hierarchical and task-oriented, competition makes up an integral part of the male gender culture. It prepares boys to take their place in the larger world by teaching them about winning and losing and being on top. Boys test themselves against each other and measure their personal adequacy in terms of where they fit in. They put each other down more than girls do as they jostle for position and self-esteem. Competition can be healthy if it gives boys an opportunity to experience themselves as doing well and if it doesn't equate not winning with failure, humiliation and shame.

When boys are young, their friendships can evolve out of rough and tumble play. As they get older, boys draw their friends from activities that they are involved in. Boys' friendships are based on loyalty and fairness. They support each other and help each other deal with problems by diffusing the emotional intensity through teasing and insults and making situations easier to handle. They cheer each other up. They offer each other advice. They show their caring not in direct words of affection or concern but indirectly and through action. Boys will be protective of those they care about. They will do things for them—do work and take on duties and responsibilities that will benefit the other.

Boys with healthy friendships are less likely to engage in risky behaviors and are more likely to do well in school. Boys who have caring friends are also less likely to be vulnerable to bullying. However, despite the emotional and social benefits of their friendships, society and its rigid code of masculinity separates boys from one because of the irrational fear of homosexuality. It limits how boys seek out and express friendship by labeling as 'weak' personal talk about problems and expressing feelings of doubt, sadness and insecurity. It prevents boys from showing affection towards one another by instilling a fear in them of being called 'fag.' When boys become friends with girls, those friendships are usually sexualized and the emotional closeness is trivialized.

DEVELOPING PROGRAMS FOR BOYS

Programs that help boys develop self-esteem and teach them healthy coping strategies must be set within the context of the male gender culture. Programs should be performance-based and contain activities such as games, projects, physical role-playing and brain-storming. They should provide boys with challenges, teach skills, and honor the ways in which boys process information and interact with one another. Boys need programs that give them a sense of mission and purpose as well as a sense of achievement. They need discipline and structure. They need to learn anger management and communication skills. They need to expand and practice their range of feelings in a safe place. Boys need opportunities to talk about and explore what it means to be male, to discuss their thoughts and opinions and share their inner emotional lives in a way that is safe and that respects and celebrates who they are. While *JUST FOR GIRLS* was designed especially for girls, parts of the program can be adapted for use with boys—so long as the language and activities are set within the context of male culture and address male biological and developmental needs.

Providing boys with a mission and purpose

Psychologist Michael Gurian writes that boys need focus, challenge and productive tasks. They also need discipline, structure and an outlet for their energy—especially during adolescence when they are dealing with frequent hormonal surges. In order to provide a balance to the developmental and societal emphasis on individualism, boys need programs and activities that provide them with a mission or purpose, with a sense that they are contributing to a collective good.

Team sports provide boys with a challenge and a mission that is greater than their individual selves and with a socially-acceptable channel for their physical energy. They teach boys self-reliance, provide a venue for their emotional development and growth and give boys a place to belong. They provide boys with friendship and with bonding and allow them to experience emotional and physical closeness with one another—so long as this intimacy takes place within the context of the activity and welfare of the team or group. Team sports can be a nurturing form of competition if they allow boys an opportunity to experience themselves as doing well. Studies show that boys who are involved with organized sports are less likely to do drugs or join gangs or become antisocial than boys who are not.

Sports systems and activities need to be supervised very carefully. Coaches and parents who teach by fear and who stress winning above all will humiliate and shame boys who do not perform well. They make boys who excel into heroes and often overlook (and therefore condone) violence and misogyny. While sports stars can be positive role models for boys, their participation in fights and in brutal body checking tells boys who are already prone to violence that this behavior is OK.

Organizations such as the Boy Scouts also provide boys with a sense of mission and purpose. They emphasize cooperation rather than competition. Like organized sports, these organizations are highly structured and hierarchical. They have a set of rules and a code of conduct. They, too, have well-defined goals and encourage interactions that are based upon loyalty and achievement.

Schools and community centers can develop similar programs and activities that address different needs and interests. These programs can encourage boys to work together cooperatively as well as compete in healthy ways and can provide boys with a tangible final product or goal. It is important that these programs combine physical activity with skill development, have clear rules, involve the participants in negotiating these rules and have a male leader who can be a role model to the boys.

Teaching anger management and communication skills

Boys need to learn how to recognize the symptoms of anger and how to channel and redirect this energy into healthy outlets so that they do not hurt other people or themselves. While sports and physical activity serve this function, so does hitting a pillow or expressing anger symbolically. Once boys have learned to deal with the intensity and immediacy of their anger, they need to learn to communicate it to others in a way that is heard and understood. Programs that teach anger management and communication and conflict resolution skills help boys do this. They also help boys increase their ability to understand other people's points of view. When boys are able to feel empathy for the weaknesses and concerns of others, they can reduce their shame about themselves. Identifying with others makes it much harder for boys to commit violence against them.

Helping boys identify and express their feelings

Boys need programs that can help them reconnect with the relational and emotional part of themselves. Boys express their feelings differently than girls do. Because they generally experience a greater time lapse between when they experience something and their recognition that it is upsetting to them, they need time to process emotional information before they can deal with it. They need to learn how to listen to their feelings and how to identify them. They need to develop a language that can help describe them.

When boys do talk about their feelings or about the things that are personal to them, they feel safest when they and the other person are engaged in a physical activity and/or are interacting side-by-side. Many boys are overwhelmed by the intensity of face-to-face interaction. They often perceive sustained eye contact as confrontation and a violation of their personal space. Programs that encourage boys to learn about and express their feelings must also include a variety of activities that are appropriate to male gender culture so that the emotional intensity and risk is diffused.

Exploring the myths of masculinity

Boys need programs that can provide them with a safe place to explore their ideas of masculinity. Boys receive conflicting messages about manhood and masculinity from their parents, their peers and from society. The traditional vision of masculinity requires boys to be aggressive, tough, independent, rational, ambitious, competitive, strong and unemotional (or able to hide emotion). The alternative vision is that of the 'sensitive' male who is empathic, egalitarian, in touch with his feelings and (except for anger and rage) expresses them openly and often. Boys have difficulty integrating a healthy vision of masculinity because the choices they are offered are polarized and contradictory. They require boys to shut down one half of themselves and exaggerate and distort the characteristics of the other. Boys need a definition of masculinity that encompasses the whole range of human feelings and behaviors, not just the ones that our society designates as male. When boys feel good about themselves and value themselves, then they don't hurt others. Nor do they allow themselves to be hurt.

FACILITATING GROUPS FOR BOYS

The facilitators of programs and groups for boys should be men who have dealt with and/or are aware of their own issues around male socialization and who can appreciate the struggles that boys have and the difficulties that they must deal with. Boys need role models and mentors who can model a broad and inclusive range of masculinity. In adolescence boys attempt to prove themselves to the male adult world. If they do not find men who model healthy masculinity and who can respect them for who they are, they will instead model themselves after boys and men who do not.

Boys crave honesty and connection. They need men in their lives who can nurture them. Often boys come from single parent homes where they have little contact with their fathers or they come from homes where their fathers are abusive or neglectful. Studies show that a boy is more likely to be empathic towards others and less likely to use violence as a way of dealing with his issues when he is able to identify with a nurturing and loving father or male role model who is able to show tenderness and empathy, who does not condone violence, and does not try to make him conform to a rigid code of masculinity.

Men who work with boys must bring their personal selves into their professional lives. They must be able to share their own experiences and vulnerabilities. This opens the door for boys to share theirs and lets them know that they don't have to be tough all of the time. It also allows boys to feel safe talking about their issues and concerns without the fear of being humiliated and shamed. Male facilitators can help boys challenge the myths of masculinity and explore their issues around power and authority. They can help boys address homophobia so that they can develop intimacy with each other and so that boys who are gay are not victimized.

Facilitators must be able to model healthy emotions so that boys can feel comfortable expressing a whole range of feelings rather than just anger and rage. They need to engage with boys when they are acting goofy, macho, aggressive, angry or rambunctious instead of correcting them and shaming them. When boys feel that they are not respected they will undermine the facilitator instead of connecting with him. A sense of humor helps boys become aware of their behavior without feeling criticized and can make it easier for boys to identify and validate their feelings of fear and inadequacy and talk about the issues that are underneath.

No two facilitators are alike nor are any two boys. Men who work with boys come from different backgrounds, have different personalities skills and interests. It is important that men trust themselves, respect the boys and help them take their place in the world.

Sources:

Michael Gurian. *The Wonder of Boys: What Parents Mentors and Educators Can Do to Shape Boys into Exceptional Men.* New York: Jeremy P. Tarcher/Putnam, 1996.

Miriam Miedzian. *Boys Will Be Boys: Breaking the Link Between Masculinity and Violence.* New York: Anchor Books, 1991.

William Pollack. *Real Boys: Rescuing Our Sons from the Myths of Boyhood.* New York: Random House, 1998.

Terrance Real. *I Don't Want to Talk About It: Overcoming the Secret Legacy of Male Depression.* New York: Scribner, 1997.

The Courage to Raise Good Men. Olga Silverstein & Beth Rashbaum. New York: Viking Penguin, 1994.

Drugs and Sport: The Score. Royal Canadian Mounted Police Drug Awareness Program.

RESOURCES

Books listed here available from:

Odin Books, 1110 West Broadway, Vancouver, BC, V6H 1G5

1-800-223-6346 ☎ 604-739–8804 🖷 604-739–8874 staff@odinbooks.bc.ca

Eating disorder subjects listed here available from:

Gürze Books, P.O. Box 2238, Carlsbad, CA 92018

1-800-756-7533 ☎ 760-434-7533 🖷 670-434-5476 gurze@aol.com

Gender and Female Development

Meeting at the Crossroads: Women's Psychology and Girls' Development. Carol Gilligan and Lyn Mikel Brown. Cambridge, Massachusetts: Harvard University Press, 1992.

Making Connections: The Relational Worlds of Adolescent Girls at Emma Willard School. Carol Gilligan, Nona P. Lyons and Trudy J. Hanmer, editors. Cambridge, Massachusetts: Harvard University Press, 1989.

Reviving Ophelia. Mary Pipher. New York: Putnam, 1994.

You Just Don't Understand: Men and Women in Conversation. Deborah Tannen. New York: Ballantine Books, 1990.

Women's Growth in Connection: Writings from the Stone Centre. Judith Jordan, Alexandra G. Kaplan, Jean Baker Miller, Irene P. Stiver and Janet L. Surrey, editors. New York: The Guilford Press, 1991.

The Brain

Sex on the Brain: The Biological Differences Between Men and Women. Deborah Blum. New York: Viking, 1997.

Brain Sex: The Real Differences Between Men and Women. Anne Moir and David Jessel. New York: Dell Publishing, 1989.

Eating Disorders

Consuming Passions: Feminist Approaches to Weight Preoccupation and Eating Disorders. Catrina Brown and Karin Jasper, editors. Toronto: Second Story Press, 1993.

Coping with Eating Disorders (a book for adolescents). Barbara Moe. New York: Rosen Publishing Group, 1991.

Surviving an Eating Disorder: Strategies for Families and Friends. Michelle Siegel, Judith Brisman and Margot Weinshel. New York: Harper Perennial, 1988.

Eating Disorder Prevention/Intervention

When Girls Feel Fat: Helping Girls Through Adolescence. Sandra Susan Friedman. Toronto: HarperCollins, 1997.

British Columbia Eating Disorders Association School Outreach Program Training Manual. Intervention with girls and women at risk.
Available from: BCEDA, 841 Fairfield Road, Victoria, BC, V8V 3B6
☎ 250-383-2755   ▦ 250-383-5518   bceda@islandnet.com

Preventing Childhood Eating Problems: A Practical Positive Approach to Raising Children Free of Food and Weight Conflicts. Jane R. Hirschmann and Lela Zaphiropoulous. California: Gürze Books, 1993.

Healthy Body Image: Teaching Kids to Eat and Love their Bodies Too! Kathy J. Kater.
A comprehensive resource manual with introductory scripted lessons for grades 4, 5 & 6.
Available from: EDAP (Eating Disorders Awareness and Prevention)
603 Stewart Street, Suite 803, Seattle, WA 98101
☎ 206-382-3587   ▦ 306-292-9890   http://members.aol.com/edapinc

Depression and Suicide

Suicide: Teens Talk to Teens. Marion Crook. Vancouver: Self-Counsel Press, 1997.

Depression is the Pits, But I'm Getting Better: A Guide for Adolescents. E. Jane Garland. Washington, DC: Magination Press, 1997.

I Don't Want to Talk About It: Overcoming the Secret Legacy of Male Depression. Terrance Real. New York: Scribner, 1997.

Sense of Self/Self Esteem

The Creative Journal for Teens. Lucia Capacchione. California: Newcastle Publishing Co., 1992.

Feed Your Head: Some Excellent Stuff on Being Yourself. Earl Hipp. Minneapolis: Hazeldon, 1991.

Ready-to-Use Self-Esteem & Conflict Solving Activities. Beth Teolis. The Centre for Applied Research in Education, 1995.

You and Self-Esteem: The Key to Happiness and Success. Betty Young. Carson, CA: Jalmar Press, 1992.

Feelings

Cage Your Rage for Teens (Workbook edition). Murray Cullen and Joan Wright. Lanham, MD: American Correctional Association, 1996.

Emotional Intelligence: Why it Can Matter More than IQ. Daniel Goleman. New York: Bantam Books, 1995.

Fighting Invisible Tigers and *Readers' Guide to Fighting Invisible Tigers.* Earl Hipp. Minneapolis: Free Spirit Publishing, 1995.

The Dance of Anger. Harriet Goldhor Lerner. New York: Harper and Row, 1986.

Thinking, Feeling, Behaving: An Emotional Education Curriculum for Adolescents. Ann Vernon. Research Press, 1993.

Stress

Stress Management and Self-Esteem Activities. Patricia Rizzo Toner. Center for Applied Research in Education, 1993.

You and Stress: A Guide for Adolescence and *Leaders' Guide to You and Your Family and School and Stress.* Gail C. Roberts and Lorraine Guttormson. Minneapolis: Free Spirit Publishing Inc. 1990.

Talk with Teens about Self and Stress. Jean Sunde Peterson. Minneapolis: Free Spirit Publishing Inc., 1993.

Bodies

The Body Image Trap: Understanding and Rejecting Body Image Myths. Marion Crook. Vancouver: Self-Counsel Press, 1991.

The Seventeen *Guide to Sex and Your Body.* Sabrina Solin with Paula Elbert, M.D.. New York: Aladdin Paperback, 1996.

What Every Teenager Really Wants to Know About Sex. Sylvia S. Hacker. New York: Carroll & Graf Publishers, Inc., 1993.

Speaking of SEX: Are You Ready to Answer the Questions Your Kids Will Ask? Meg Hickling, Kelowna, B.C.: Northstone Publishing Inc, 1996.

What's Happening to My Body? Book for Girls and *Book for Boys* [1984]
My Body, Myself [1993]. Lynda Madaras. New York: Newmarket Press.

Physical Activity and Sports

The Bodywise Woman: Reliable Information about Physical Activity and Health [1990].
   The Melpomene Institute, 1010 University Avenue, St. Paul MN 55104
   ☎ 612-642-1951   🖷 612-642-1871   www.melpomene.org

Promoting Fitness and Self-Esteem in Your Overweight Child. Teresa Pitman and Miram Kaufman. M.D.. Toronto: HarperPerennial, 1994.

On the Move: Increasing Participation of Girls and Women in Physical Activity and Sport (Manual). A program designed to encourage non-active adolescent girls to participate in fun-filled supportive, low skill level, team recreational activity.
Available from: Promotion Plus, #305-1367 West Broadway, Vancouver, BC V6H 4A9
            ☎ 604-737-3075   🖷 604-738-7175   promplus@mindlink.bc.ca

Diets and Weight

When Women Stop Hating Their Bodies: Freeing Yourself from Food and Weight Obsession. Jane R. Hirschmann and Carol H. Munter. New York: Fawcett Columbine/Ballantine Books, 1995.

Making Peace with Food: Freeing Yourself from the Diet/Weight Obsession. Susan Kano. New York: Harper & Row, 1989.

Communication/Conflict Resolution

Skillstreaming the Adolescent: New Strategies and Perspectives for Teaching Prosocial Skills and *Skillstreaming the Adolescent Student Manual.* Arnold P. Goldstein and Ellen McGinnis. Research Press, 1997.

Viewpoints: A Guide to Conflict Resolution and Decision Making for Adolescents and *Teachers' Guide to Viewpoints.* Nancy G. Guerra, Ann Moore and Ronald Slaby. Research Press, 1995.

Peer Mediation: Conflict Resolution in Schools (Program Guide and Student Manual). Fred Schrumpf, Donna Crawford and Richard Bodine. Research Press, 1996.

Relationships

Where You and I Begin. Anne Katherine, New York: Fireside Books, 1993.

Dating Violence: Young Women and Danger. Barrie Levy, editor. Seattle: Seal Press, 1991.

Teen Talk: Scenarios for Discussions about Problem Solving, Decision Making, Relationship-Building, Help Seeking and Communication.
   King County Sexual Assault Resource Centre, P.O. Box 300, Renton, WA 98057
   ☎ 425-226-5062   🖷 425-235-7422   information@kcsarc.org   www.kcsarc.org

Relationships and Communication Activities. Patricia Rizzo Toner. The Centre for Applied Research in Education, 1996.

The Dance of Intimacy. Harriet Goldhor Lerner. New York: Harper & Row, 1989.

School

SchoolGirls: Young Women, Self-Esteem and the Confidence Gap. Peggy Orenstein in association with the American Association of University Women. New York: Doubleday, 1994.

Failing At Fairness: How Our Schools Cheat Girls. Myra Sadker and David Sadker. New York: Touchstone, 1994.

Media

Real Gorgeous: The Truth about Body and Beauty. Kaz Cooke. NSW, Australia: Allen & Unwin, 1994.

Where the Girls Are: Growing Up Female with the Mass Media. Susan J. Douglas. New York: Random House, 1994.

No Fat Chicks: How Women are Brainwashed to Hate their Bodies and Spend their Money. Terry Poulton, Toronto: Key Porter Books Ltd., 1996.

Bullying, Violence and Aggression

Sex, Power and the Violent School Girl. Sibylle Artz. Toronto: Trifolium Books, Inc. 1998.

Bully Proofing Your School. Carla Garrity et al. Longmont, CO: 1994.

Take Action Against Bullying, [1997] Gesele Lajoie, Alyson McLellan and Cindi Seddon.
Available from: Bully B'ware Productions, 1421 King Albert Avenue, Coquitlam, BC, V3J 1Y3
        1-888-55BULLY   ☎+🖶 604-936-8000

When She was Bad: Violent Women and the Myth of Innocence. Patricia Pearson. Toronto: Random House, 1997.

Safe Teen: the Girls' Program and *Safe: Teen: the Boys' Program: A Life Skills and Violence Prevention Program.* Contact: Anita Roberts, Program Director.   ☎+🖶 604-255-5147

Bullyproof: A Teacher's Guide on Teasing and Bullying for Use with Fourth and Fifth Grade Students. Nan Stein, Emily Gaberman, Lisa Sjostrom and Dominic Cappello. NEA, 1996.

Alternatives to Violence: Empowering Youth to Develop Healthy Relationships. David A. Wolfe, Christine Wekerle and Katreena Scott. California: Sage Publications, 1996.

Battling the School-Yard Bully: How to Raise an Assertive Child in an Aggressive World. Kim Zarzour. Toronto: HarperPerennial, 1994.

Boys

The Wonder of Boys: What Parents Mentors and Educators Can Do to Shape Boys into Exceptional Men. Michael Gurian. New York: Jeremy P. Tarcher/Putnam, 1996.

Boys Will Be Boys: Breaking the Link Between Masculinity and Violence. Miriam Miedzian. New York: Anchor Books, 1991.

The Courage to Raise Good Men. Olga Silverstein & Beth Rashbaum. New York: Viking Penguin, 1994.

Real Boys: Rescuing Our Sons from the Myths of Boyhood. William Pollack, New York: Random House, 1998.

MAGAZINES

In 2 Print. P.O. Box 102, Port Colborne, ON, L3K 5V7   Publishes original works by young male and female adults (12 to 20) including poetry, short stories, one-act plays, painting, photography, computer art and cartoons.   1-888-215-5142   ☎ 905-834–1539   🖷 905-834–1540

Reluctant Hero Magazine. (Girls 13–16) 189 Lonsmount Drive, Toronto, ON, M5P 2Y6
☎ 416-656-8047

New Moon: The Magazine for Girls and Their Dreams (Girls 8–12)   www.newmoon.org
New Moon Publishing, P.O. Box 3587, Duluth, MN   55803-3587
1-800-381-4743   ☎ 218-728-5507   🖷 218-728-0314   newmoon@newmoon.duluth.mn.us

Daughters: a newsletter for parents of girls (8 to 18)
1808 Ashwood Avenue, Nashville, TN 37212
☎ 615-297-4778   🖷 615-297-9129   daughter1@aol.com

FILM/VIDEO

Model Perfect from *READY OR NOT* series
'Amanda' and 'Bizzy' – great appeal in story format for Grades 5 – 7
distributor: McNabb and Connolly, 60 Briarwood Avenue, Port Credit, ON L5G 3N6
☎ 905-278-2801   🖷 905-278-0566

TAKE ANOTHER LOOK [1994] 24 minutes
produced by: Lisa O'Brien and Bernice Vanderlaan
distributor: McNabb and Connolly
   This film is a dramatic fantasy on self esteem for viewers aged 11-13. It encourages discussion on self-esteem, body image, the beauty and diet industries, self-respect and the need for peer support.

KILLING US SOFTLY: ADVERTISING'S IMAGE OF WOMEN [1979] 28:00 minutes
produced by: Cambridge Documentary Films
distributor: National Film Board of Canada (catalog # 0179 389)
   American feminist Jean Kilbourne casts a critical eye on the power and influence of advertising.

STILL KILLING US SOFTLY [1987] 30:00 minutes
produced by: Cambridge Documentary Films
distributor: National Film Board of Canada (catalog # 0187 145)
   This sequel to *KILLING US SOFTLY* offers tools for developing a critical approach to mass media.

SLIM HOPES: MEDIA'S OBESSION WITH THINNESS [1995] 29 minutes
Another Jean Kilbourne film - excellent for high school
Available through: Kinetic Video Inc., 409 Dundas East, Toronto, ON M5A 2A5
      1-800-263-6910   ☎ 416-963-5979   🖷416-925-0653

BEYOND THE LOOKING GLASS 28 minutes
Grade 8–10 teacher resource (can be used for younger girls) produced in the U.S.. Focuses on self-esteem, thoughts, feelings, identification of attitudes, stereotypes, body image and provides direction to garner support for problem solving.
Available through: McIntyre Media, 30 Kelfield Street, Rexdale, ON M9W 5A1
      1-800-565-3036   🖷 416-245-8660

SESSION PLANS

Session Plan S-1: Introduction to the Program

Objectives: The girls will...

✓ Understand what the group is about.
✓ Become familiar with the Talking Stick.
✓ Develop group rules.
✓ Choose topics for future sessions
✓ Be introduced to the *grungies*.
✓ Fill out the *Tell Us About You* form.

Materials:

❏ Talking Stick or substitute
❏ Flip chart
❏ Felt pens
❏ Journals (e.g., binders)
❏ *Tell Us About You* form H-4
❏ *Grungie* handout H-5
❏ Snack

The Group Session

Welcome: Welcome the girls to the group. Tell them a little about yourself. Make sure that you include something personal. Tell the girls that this is a time for them to talk about their concerns. Reassure them that they cannot fail. Ask girls to introduce themselves and to say one personal thing about themselves.

Talking Stick: Introduce the concept of the Talking Stick. Let the girls know that they will use it each time that they have a discussion.

Rules: Have the girls choose the group rules and write them on the flip chart. You can make suggestions of the things that you want included. Keep the rules few and simple. Practice using the Talking Stick.

Topics: Chose the group topics. Remind girls that the group is a place to discuss their concerns. Ask them about these concerns and write them on your flip chart. You can make suggestions, too. Vote on the topics.

Grungies: Introduce girls to the *grungies* and the *grungie* circle. Encourage each girl to talk about something that bugs her.

Journals: Give each girl a journal. Assure them all that their journals are private. They can write stories and poems, draw pictures and write about their feelings and *grungies*. They can also put any handouts from the group into their journal. The journal will become a part of each week's session.

Tell Us About You: Have the girls fill out the form *Tell Us About You* form H-4.

Close: Close the group by asking each girl to describe one thing she likes about being a girl.

[Note: The best time to have a break depends upon the energy level of the group—depending on whether it is low and you want to revive the girls, or if it is too high you might need to tone them down.]

Session Plan S-2: Self and Self-esteem

Objectives: The girls will...

✓ Practice decoding the *grungies*.
✓ Develop an understanding of the concepts *self* and *self-esteem*.
✓ Explore their own feelings about themselves.

Materials:

❑ Pens or pencils
❑ Journals
❑ *Building a Healthy Sense of Self* handout H-7
❑ *Valuing My Personal Strengths* handout H-8
❑ Snack, box of tissues

The Group Session

Opening the Session: Welcome the girls to the group. Reassure them that they cannot fail. Review the group rules. Ask the girls if there is anything from the last session that they would like to talk about or anything from their journal that they would like to share.

The Grungie Circle: Review the concept of *grungies* (H-5). Ask each girl to remember a time in the past week when she was 'hit by a *grungie*.' Help her explore what is underneath. Act out the *grungies*: divide the girls into groups of three. Have each group chose an 'actor.' Have that person explain to the other two girls what parts she wants them to play in her scenario. Act out the *grungies* but change the endings to state the real feelings instead of feeling fat.

Session Topic: *Self* and *Self-Esteem*

1. **Building a Sense of Self:** Explain the concept of self. Introduce handout H-7 *Building a Healthy Sense of Self*. Talk about how each girl lives within the context of, and is affected by, her relationship with all of the components of the diagram including the world in which we live. Beginning with *ME* go through the diagram and ask girls to suggest issues and concerns that affect or are the result of relationships between each section.

2. **Valuing My Personal Strengths:** Explain the concept of *self-esteem*. Talk about how most girls derive their self-esteem from how they look and forget about the other things that make them feel good about themselves. Ask them to suggest some of these things. Tell the girls that we need to know about our personal strengths so that we can remember them when we feel fat. Have each girl fill out handout H-8 *Valuing My Personal Strengths*. If girls have difficulty, have them insert it into their journals and come back to it sometime during the week.

3. **A Typical Day in My Life:** Divide girls into groups of three. Have each girl tell her sub-group about a typical day in her life. Remind the girls that every time they say 'I' they are building their sense of self. (Optional if there is time.)

Closing the Session: Have each girl share two things about herself that make her interesting.

Session Plan S-3: Understanding and Expressing Our Feelings

Objectives: The girls will...

✓ Practice decoding the *grungies*.
✓ Develop the ability to recognize and describe a variety of feelings that affect their thoughts and behavior.

Materials:

❑ Pens or pencils
❑ Journals
❑ *Building a Feeling Vocabulary* handout H-10
❑ *Playing Feeling Charades* handout H-11
❑ Snacks, box of tissues

The Group Session

Opening the Session: Welcome the girls to the group. Reassure them that they cannot fail. Review the group rules. Ask the girls if there is anything from the last session that they would like to talk about or anything from their journal that they would like to share.

The Grungie Circle: Review the concept of *grungies* (H-5). Ask each girl to remember a time in the past week when she was 'hit by a *grungie*' and help her explore what is underneath. Ask her what she would like to have said if she didn't have to worry about being 'nice' or hurting someone else.

Session Topic: Understanding and Expressing Our Feelings

1. **Building a Feeling Vocabulary:** Go over the list *Building a Feeling Vocabulary* H-10 and determine which of the feelings the girls can identify. Add to the list the slang words that girls use to describe feelings (e.g. stoked, pumped, choked, etc.). Have each girl chose a feeling and use it in a sentence. After every girl has had a turn, go around the group again.

2. **Playing Feeling Charades:** Cut out *feeling squares* of *Playing Feeling Charades* H-11 and separate them into three piles according to difficulty. Divide the girls into groups of three. Have each group select a feeling from the appropriate pile and chose a girl to act it out. If the actor is having difficulty, she can ask her sub-group for help. If the audience is having difficulty identifying the feeling, tell them if the feeling is a 'good' feeling or a 'bad' one.

Closing the Session: Have each girl share two things that are important to her.

Session Plan S-4: Expressing Anger

Objectives: The girls will...

✓ Practice decoding the *grungies*.
✓ Develop an understanding of the different ways in which people express anger.
✓ Develop skills for expressing their anger in a healthy way.

Materials:

❑ Pens or pencils
❑ *Dead flowers* (or box of tissues)
❑ Journals
❑ Snacks, box of tissues

The Group Session

Opening the Session: Welcome the girls to the group. Reassure them that they cannot fail. Review the group rules. Ask the girls if there is anything from the last session that they would like to talk about, or anything from their journal that they would like to share.

Grungie Circle: Review the concept of *grungies* (H-5). Ask each girl to remember a time in the past week when she was 'hit by a *grungie*' and help her explore what is underneath. Ask her what she would like to say if she didn't have to worry about being 'nice' or hurting someone's feelings.

Session Topic: Expressing Our Anger

1. **Recognizing Anger:** All feelings are energy. Anger is a form of energy. Ask the girls to think of a time when they were angry. Where could they feel the anger in their body? Ask the girls what happens to the energy when you can't let it out. What are some ways that we can let out the angry energy without hurting someone else? Tell the girls that sometimes we don't know we are angry. We find out from some of the things that we tell ourselves. What are some of the clues that let you know that you are angry? Sometimes we are angry but don't know how to express it effectively. Look at some ways people express their anger badly and why these ways don't work. (e.g. media, sports figures, experiences from family and friends) Look at positive ways that people express their anger. What is the difference?

2. **Saying Yes and No:** This exercise allows girls to use their bodies to express their feelings. On the count of three have the girls clench their fists and jump up into the air. As they come down have them yell 'No!' as loud as they can. Repeat two more times. Do the same exercise having them jump up as high as they can and reach for the ceiling. As they come down, have them yell, 'Yes!' as loud as they can. Ask them which is easier for them.

↘

3. **Hold a 'Dead Flower Ceremony':** Let the girls know that sometimes when we get angry or feel hurt and disappointed with people it's too scary for us to tell them directly how we are feeling. If we keep the feelings inside, they turn into *grungies* so we need to express them. A safe way to do that is to talk to the person symbolically when they are not actually there and can't react.

- ◆ Have the girls bring in dead flowers or make flowers out of tissues. Have the girls think of someone that they are angry with. If anger is hard for some girls then use words such as annoyed, just a little bit upset, etc. Ask them to think about what they would like to say to the person if they were not afraid of hurting them or being hurt themselves.

- ◆ Place a garbage can in the center of the room. Have each girl stand in front of the garbage can, say out loud what she would like to say to that person and then throw the flower and her feelings into the can. Once she has said what she needs to say, she can let the feelings go.

- ◆ If you are doing this exercise with a large group, have the girls write what they want to say on the paper (or tissues) instead of saying it out loud, then throw the flower and feelings away.

Closing the Session: Have each girl share two things that she values about herself.

Session Plan S-5: Dealing with Stress

Objectives: The girls will...

✓ Practice decoding the *grungies*.
✓ Develop an understanding of what stress is, and identify the stressors in their lives.
✓ Develop skills for dealing with stress in a healthy way.

Materials:

❑ Pens or pencils, and felt pens
❑ Journals
❑ Drawing paper
❑ Snacks, box of tissues

The Group Session

Opening the Session: Welcome the girls to the group. Reassure them that they cannot fail. Review the group rules. Ask the girls if there is anything from the last session that they would like to talk about or anything from their journal that they would like to share.

Grungie Circle: Review the concept of *grungies* (H-5). Ask each girl to remember a time in the past week when she was 'hit by a *grungie*' instead of being angry. Act out the *grungies*: divide the girls into groups of three. Have each group chose one girl to act out her *grungie*. Have her explain to the other girls what parts she wants them to play in her scenario. Have her change the ending so that she can express what she really feels instead of feeling fat.

Session Topic: Dealing with Stress

1. **Identifying Stress:** Ask the girls if they know what *stress* means. Ask them to think of one situation where they felt stressed. Ask the girls how they know that they are under stress. What are the symptoms? How do they behave? How do they feel? How does their body react?

2. **Drawing a Stress Tree:** Give each girl a sheet of drawing paper. Have the girls draw a large tree trunk. Have them think of things, people or situations that cause them to feel stressed. Ask them to draw and label a leaf for every one of these situations. Divide the girls into groups of three. Have them compare their trees. Ask them to make a list of the stresses that they have in common and a list of the ones that are different. Have them share their answers with the larger group. Discuss strategies for coping with stress.

Closing the Session: Have girls give each other verbal bouquets that address a situation in their lives. Girls can make statements such as 'I would like to give Mary ear plugs so that she doesn't have to listen to her brother's music.'

Session Plan S-6: Talking About Puberty

[Note: The week before this session, tell the girls that this session will be about puberty. Give the girls index cards and have them write down whatever questions they would like to ask. Put the questions into an envelope so that the questions are anonymous. Look up the answers before the session.]

Objectives: The girls will...

✓ Practice decoding the *grungies*.
✓ Have an opportunity to talk about their concerns about the emotional and physical changes in their bodies.

Materials:

❑ Index cards (the week previous)
❑ Envelope (with questions)
❑ Pens or pencils
❑ Journals
❑ Snacks, box of tissues

The Group Session

Opening the Session: Welcome the girls to the group. Reassure them that they cannot fail. Review the group rules. Ask the girls if there is anything from the last session that they would like to talk about or anything from their journal that they would like to share.

Grungie Circle: Review the concept of *grungies* (H-5). Ask each girl to remember a time in the past week when she was 'hit by a grungie.' Encourage the girls to talk about what is underneath their grungie.

Session Topic: Dealing with Puberty

1. **Talking about Puberty:** Tell the girls that puberty can sometimes be a difficult experience and that even though it can be hard to talk about it, we need to know everything we can about our bodies—because they are the only bodies we are ever going to get.

2. **Normalize Their Fears:** Tell the girls that no two girls go through puberty at the same time and in the same way. Everyone feels that they are not normal and are the only ones who feel that way. Talk about early and late bloomers and the stresses girls experience in each.

3. **Taboos:** Defuse subjects that are taboo. Ask the girls if they ever noticed how sometimes we make a big fuss over a guy who is growing a mustache for the first time, but are embarrassed about our periods when we get them. Ask how many of them would come into class announcing 'I got my period, I got my period!'

4. **Questions:** Read out the questions in the envelopes and answer them. Tell the girls that if you can't answer their questions today, you'll look up the answers for next week. Bring in or suggest books about puberty that the girls can read.

Closing the Session: Have girls give each other verbal bouquets about what makes them interesting, fun, different, etc.

Session Plan S-7: Body Image/Body Awareness #1

Objectives: The girls will...

✓ Practice decoding the *grungies*.
✓ Develop an understanding of what body image is.
✓ Develop an awareness of their own attitudes towards their bodies.
✓ Develop an awareness of their bodies that goes beyond their external image.

Materials:

❏ Pens or pencils
❏ Flip Chart
❏ Journals
❏ *How I Feel About my Body* handout H-12
❏ Snacks, box of tissues

The Group Session

Opening the Session: Welcome the girls to the group. Reassure them that they cannot fail. Review the group rules. Ask the girls if there is anything from the last session that they would like to talk about or anything from their journal that they would like to share.

Grungie Circle: Review the concept of *grungies* (H-5). Ask each girl to recount a time in the past week when she was 'hit by a *grungie*.'

Session Topic: Body Image/Body Awareness

1. **My Body Type:** Tell the girls that bodies come in all shapes, colors and sizes. They also come in three distinct types:

   Endomorphs tend to have rounder body types, with more body fat and softer curves.
   Ectomorphs are slim, less curvy, more angular.
   Mesomorphs are muscular, with wide shoulders and slim hips.

   Sometimes these body types overlap but ask the girls if they can guess what type they are. What type are their mothers, fathers? Tell girls that different body types do better at different physical activities. What kind of physical activities make them feel good? Make them feel awkward?

2. **How I Feel About My Body:** Explain the concept of body image. Tell the girls that we grow up with different feelings and attitudes about our bodies. Divide the group up into pairs or into groups of three. Have each girl do her own body attitude inventory H-12. Have the girls discuss their answers in the small groups. Have them share their answers for questions 1-6 in the large group. Talk about how putting your body down is another kind of *grungie*.

3. **The Perfect Girl:** Ask the girls to describe the perfect girl. List the descriptions on the flip chart. Talk about the pressures to have a certain type of body. Remind girls that telling themselves they should be perfect is also a *grungie*, and that every time that they do this they are usually feeling something else such as insecure, angry, etc.

Closing the Session: Have each girl describe a part of her body where she feels strong.

Session Plan S-8: Body Image/Body Awareness #2

Objectives: The girls will...

✓ Practice decoding the *grungies*.
✓ Develop an understanding of or review what body image is.
✓ Develop an awareness of their bodies that goes beyond their external image.

Materials:

❑ Pens or pencils, and felt pens
❑ Roll of drawing paper
❑ Journals
❑ Snacks, box of tissues

The Group Session

Opening the Session: Welcome the girls to the group. Reassure them that they cannot fail. Review the group rules. Ask the girls if there is anything from the last session that they would like to talk about or anything from their journal that they would like to share.

Grungie Circle: Review the concept of *grungies* (H-5). Ask each girl to remember a time in the past week when she was 'hit by a *grungie*.' Encourage the girls to talk about what is underneath.

Session Topic: Body Image/Body Awareness

1. **Developing Body Awareness:** Tell girls that how we hold our bodies can influence how we feel as well as the opposite. Ask the girls to walk around the room as if they are depressed, as if they won the lottery, in a 'masculine' way, in a 'feminine' way. How does their body change each time? Ask girls to think of situations when they felt really small. Did that make them feel powerless? What else were they feeling? Ask them to stretch up tall and imagine that situation. How do they feel? Ask them when they felt really big. What else were they feeling? Did they feel that they took up too much space? How did that feel?

2. **Drawing our Bodies:** Using rolls of heavy paper, have girls draw an outline of each other's body.

   Part 1: Have girls use different color felt pens or crayons to color in these different parts: The parts that they use a lot. The parts that they really like. Those body parts that are the strongest, those that are the weakest. The parts that they have confidence in—that work well when they want them to. The parts that make them feel embarrassed. The parts that give them pain. The parts where they hold their stress.

   Part 2: Ask the girls to imagine a situation where they felt sad, insecure, angry, hurt, disappointed, happy and content. Using different colored felt pens, ask the girls to color in those places in their bodies where they feel the feelings. You might have to do this activity over two sessions. You can do Part 1 or Part 2, or do both. Remember that there is no right or wrong.

Closing the Session: Have each girl share two things that she appreciates about her body.

Session Plan S-9: Our Relationship with Food

Objectives: The girls will...

✓ Practice decoding the *grungies*.
✓ Develop an understanding of their eating habits.
✓ Develop an understanding about the myths around food.

Materials:

❑ Pens or pencils
❑ *Flower Pot* handout H-9
❑ *Exploring Your Eating Habits* handout H-13
❑ Journals
❑ Snacks, box of tissues

The Group Session

Opening the Session: Welcome the girls to the group. Reassure them that they cannot fail. Review the group rules. Ask girls if there is anything from the last session that they would like to talk about or anything from their journal that they would like to share.

Grungie Circle: Review the concept of the *grungies* (H-5). Ask each girl to remember a time in the past week when she was 'hit by a *grungie*.' Act out the *grungie*: divide the girls into groups of three. Have each group decide on an actor. Have that person explain the parts she wants the other girls to play. Act out the *grungie* and change the ending to find the real feelings instead of feeling fat.

Session Topic: Our Relationship With Food

1. **The Food We Eat:** Tell the girls that we often have different beliefs about the food that we eat. For example, we learn to divide food into 'good' food and 'bad' food and 'healthy' food and 'junk' food. Ask for examples of each. Ask them when they eat 'good' food and 'healthy' food or 'bad' food and 'junk' food. We also think that having fat in our diet is bad. Explain that girls need a balance in their diets. They also need fat, especially when they are going through puberty and growing. Talk about skipping breakfast and how that makes them feel. Talk about the rules that different families have about eating and about different foods.

2. **Exploring Your Eating Habits:** Tell girls that we all have different eating habits. Often we eat when we are not hungry and we usually eat certain foods when we have certain feelings. Have the girls fill out the handout H-13 *Exploring Your Eating Habits* and discuss their answers in the larger group. Encourage the girls to be curious about when and why they are eating when they are not hungry, and have them report their answers to the group. It is important that you validate whatever their choices may be—so that they don't feel different nor feel that what they are doing is wrong.

Closing the Session: Give each girl a *Flower Pot* (H-9) and two Post-It Notes. Have each girl give 'flowers' to half of the girls in the group by writing feedback about these girls on the Post-It Notes and sticking them on the stems of the other girls' *Flower Pots*. Collect the *Flower Pots* for future use.

Session Plan S-10: Exploring the Myths about Dieting

Objectives: The girls will...

✓ Practice decoding the *grungies*.
✓ Develop an understanding of the myths about dieting
✓ Develop an understanding about what happens when we diet.

Materials:

❑ Pens or pencils
❑ *Flower Pot* handout H-9
❑ *Exploring the Myths about Dieting* handout H-14
❑ *What Really Happens When We Diet* handout H-15
❑ Journals
❑ Snacks, box of tissues

The Group Session

Opening the Session: Welcome the girls to the group. Reassure them that they cannot fail. Review the group rules. Ask girls if there is anything from the last session that they would like to talk about or anything from their journal that they would like to share.

Grungie Circle: Review the concept of the *grungies* (H-5). Ask each girl to remember a time in the past week when she was 'hit by a *grungie*.' Act out the *grungie*: divide the girls into groups of three. Have each group decide on an actor. Have that person explain the parts she wants the other girls to play. Act out the *grungie* and change the ending to find the real feelings instead of feeling fat.

Session Topic: Exploring the Myths about Dieting

1. **The Pressures to be Thin:** Talk about the perfect girl. What makes her perfect? Talk about the pressures that girls are under to be thin and the anxiety that they feel. Talk about the pressures to be perfect and therefore self-confident. Is this realistic? Ask the girls when they feel this anxiety.

2. **Exploring the Myths About Dieting:** Tell girls that sometimes we think that because there is so much pressure to be thin, that being fat is bad. When we get really panicky about feeling fat we sometimes try to change our bodies by dieting. Many of the things that we are led to believe about being fat or thin, about dieting, and about the foods that we eat are not true. Have the girls do handout H-14 and discuss the answers in the group.

3. **What Really Happens When We Diet:** Continue the discussion with handout H-15. If it is appropriate, you might want to talk about how diets can lead to disordered eating, anorexia, bulimia and compulsive eating. Do not describe the details of the behaviors. Talk about how girls use food and the preoccupation with weight as a way of dealing with feelings and with stressors in their lives.

Closing the Session: Using the *Flower Pot* (H-9) have each girl give flowers to the rest of the girls in the group..

Session Plan S-11: Learning Good Communication Skills #1

Objectives: The girls will...

✓ Practice decoding the *grungies*.
✓ Learn about communication and about making 'I' statements.
✓ Learn about being assertive.
✓ Develop skills for making assertive statements and dealing with situations assertively.

Materials:

❑ Pens or pencils
❑ Journals
❑ *Making Assertive Statements* handout H-16
❑ *Responding Assertively to Situations* handout H-17
❑ Snacks, box of tissues

The Group Session

Opening the Session: Welcome the girls to the group. Reassure them that they cannot fail. Review the group rules. Ask the girls if there is anything from the last session that they would like to talk about or anything from their journals that they would like to share.

Grungie Circle: Review the concept of *grungies* (H-5). Ask each girl to remember a time in the past week when she was 'hit by a *grungie*' and help her explore what is underneath.

Session Topic: Learning Good Communication Skills

1. **'I' and 'You' Statements:** Ask the girls if they know what communication is, how it works, and if they know different ways to communicate. Tell them that good communication means that we can talk and listen to each other in such a way that we understand what it is like for the other person. Explain the difference between 'I' and 'you' statements. Practice making some of each. Ask the girls how it feels when someone says 'I' and 'you.'

2. **Making Assertive Statements:** Explain what being assertive means. Talk about the do's and don'ts. Divide the girls into groups of three. Have each group do the handout H-16 *Making Assertive Statements.* Have each girl act out an assertive statement for the larger group. Make sure that they all don't choose the same ones.

3. **Responding Assertively to Situations:** Divide the girls into groups of three. Photocopy and cut apart the scenarios in the handout H-17 *Responding Assertively to Situations.* Give different scenarios to each group. Have them act them out. After each performance encourage the audience to talk about how they might have handled the situation. If there is not enough time to complete the activity in this session, continue it the following week.

Closing the Session: Have each girl share something that she likes about herself.

Session Plan S-12: Learning Good Communication Skills #2

Objectives: The girls will...

✓ Practice decoding the *grungies*.
✓ Learn and practice how to give feedback.
✓ Learn how to fight fairly.

Materials:

❑ Pens or pencils
❑ Journals
❑ *Responding Assertively to Situations* handout H-17
❑ *Telling Someone How Their Behavior Makes Us Feel* H-18
❑ *Rules for Good Communication...* handout H-19
❑ Snacks, box of tissues

The Group Session

Opening the Session: Welcome the girls to the group. Reassure them that they cannot fail. Review the group rules. Ask the girls if there is anything from the last session that they would like to talk about or anything from their journal that they would like to share.

Grungie Circle: Review the concept of *grungies* (H-5). Ask each girl to remember a time in the past week when she was 'hit by a grungie' and help her explore what is underneath.

Session Topic: Learning Good Communication Skills

1. **Responding Assertively to Situations**: Review 'I' and 'you' statements and how to respond assertively to situations. Divide the girls into groups of three. Have each group act out a scenario from the handout H-17 *Responding Assertively to Situations.*

2. **Telling Someone How Their Behavior Makes You Feel.** Explain that sometimes being assertive and telling someone what you want is not enough. You need to tell them how their behavior makes you feel. This is called giving *feedback*. Review the do's and don'ts for giving feedback. Have the girls think of a situation when they wanted someone to change their behavior. What would they say? Tell the girls that they also need to know how to deal with the other person's response. Sometimes the other person feels criticized and defensive. Talk about how to deal with defensiveness. Give each girl a copy of the handout H-19 *Rules for Good Communication and for Fighting Fairly*. Review the rules with them.

3. **Giving Each Other Feedback**: Divide the girls into groups of three. Cut apart the scenarios in the handout H-18 *Telling Someone How Their Behavior Makes You Feel*. Give different scenarios to each group. Have them act them out. After each performance encourage the audience to talk about how they might have handled the situation.

Closing the Session: Have each girl share something that she does well.

Session Plan S-13: Families

Objectives: The girls will...

✓ Practice decoding the *grungies*.
✓ Define who makes up their family
✓ Develop an understanding of the rules and values of their families
✓ Practice dealing with conflict

Materials:

❑ Pens or pencils, and felt pens
❑ Flip chart
❑ Drawing paper
❑ *All Kinds of Families* handout H-20
❑ Journals
❑ Snacks, box of tissues

The Group Session

Opening the Session: Welcome the girls to the group. Reassure them that they cannot fail. Review the group rules. Ask the girls if there is anything from the last session that they would like to talk about or anything from their journal that they would like to share.

Grungie Circle: Review the concept of *grungies* (H-5). Ask each girl to remember a time in the past week when she was 'hit by a *grungie*' and help her explore what is underneath.

Session Topic: Families

1. **All Kinds of Families:** Tell the girls that children come from all kinds of families. Go over handout H-20 and ask them to identify the kind of family that they come from. Ask them if they know other families that look like some of these examples. Even if families are different in structure, what do they have in common?

2. **Exploring Rules and Values:** Give each girl a sheet of drawing paper. Have them divide the sheet into two columns. Label one column 'My Family's Values' and the other column 'My Values.' Explain that each family has its own set of rules and values. Have them list their family's rules and values in one column. Have them list their own rules and values in the other. Discuss what the rules and values are, how they differ in families and cultures. Ask the girls which of their own values agree/disagree with their family's values.

3. **Family Conflict:** Divide the girls into groups of three. Using the communication skills that the girls have learned, have one girl in each group act out and resolve a conflict with a family member. Have the second girl be that family member and the third girl ensure that good communication rules are being followed. If there is time, have the other girls act out their conflicts.

Closing the Session: Have each girl share with the group something that makes her a valuable member of her family.

Session Plan S-14: Friendships

[Note: You might want to extend this over two sessions and role-play dealing with conflict in each session.]

Objectives: The girls will...

✓ Practice decoding the *grungies*.
✓ Develop an understanding of the qualities that they value in friendship.
✓ Develop an understanding of the qualities in themselves that make them a good friend.
✓ Develop an understanding of the dark side of friendship.
✓ Practice dealing with conflict.

Materials:

❑ Pens or pencils, and felt pens
❑ Flip chart
❑ Drawing paper
❑ Journals
❑ Snacks, box of tissues

The Group Session

Opening the Session: Welcome the girls to the group. Reassure them that they cannot fail. Review the group rules. Ask the girls if there is anything from the last session that they would like to talk about or anything from their journal that they would like to share.

Grungie Circle: Review the concept of *grungies* (H-5). Ask each girl to remember a time in the past week when she was 'hit by a *grungie*' and help her explore what is underneath.

Session Topic: Relationships with Other Girls

1. **What I Want in a Friend:** Give each girl a sheet of drawing paper. Have her divide it into two sections. Label Section 1 'What I Want in a Friend.' Label Section 2 'Qualities That I Should Have.' Talk about some of the qualities that we look for in our friends, and about how we sometimes find ourselves lacking certain qualities that we would expect in a good friend. Have the girls fill out both columns. Have them put a check mark next to the qualities in Section 1 that they think they have. Have them put X next to the qualities in Section 2 that they don't have. Write the same headings on a flip chart. Have the girls call out the qualities for both charts. Discuss the differences in the charts and what they mean.

2. **The Dark Side of Friendship:** Talk about how girls feel insecure about their friendships. Ask the girls for examples of how girls hurt each other. Talk about the dark side of friendship.

3. **Conflict with Friends:** Divide the girls into groups of three. Using the communication skills that the girls have learned, have one girl in each group act out and resolve a conflict with a friend. Have the second girl be the friend and the third girl ensure that good communication rules are being followed. Have the girls change places and act out another girl's conflict. Do it once more if there is time.

Closing the Session: Have each girl share two things that make her a good friend.

Session Plan S-15: Choosing a Partner

Objectives: The girls will...

✓ Practice decoding the *grungies*.
✓ Have an opportunity to talk about choosing a partner.
✓ Develop an understanding of the qualities that they should look for in a partner.

Materials:

❑ Pens or pencils
❑ *Choosing a Partner* handout H-22
❑ Journals
❑ Snacks, box of tissues

The Group Session

Opening the Session: Welcome the girls to the group. Reassure them that they cannot fail. Review the group rules. Ask the girls if there is anything from the last session that they would like to talk about or anything from their journal that they would like to share.

Grungie Circle: Review the concept of *grungies* (H-5). Ask each girl to remember a time in the past week when she was 'hit by *a grungie*.' Have her retell her story without the grungie but with the real feeling.

Session Topic: Choosing a Partner

1. **Discussion Concerning Relationships with Boys**: Girls love to talk about boys. The nature of your discussion will depend upon the age group of the girls. Topics you might choose to discuss: gender differences in the ways in which girls and boys relate to one another; how girls blame themselves when they feel uncomfortable with a boy instead of looking at the dynamics that create the discomfort; how hard it is to say 'no' and why; questions girls might have about relationships with boys; the double standard. (If you are comfortable with the subject, you can consider discussing sexuality and the choices that girls make, and why they make these choices.)

2. **My Ideal Partner**: Acknowledge that not all girls choose boys as partners. Some girls choose other girls. Talk about how girls wait to be chosen instead of doing the choosing. Have the girls do handout H-22. Discuss the answers.

Closing the Session: Have each girl share the two most important things that she would want in a partner.

Session Plan S-16: Relationships with Boys

Objectives: The girls will...

✓ Practice decoding the *grungies.*
✓ Practice saying 'yes' and 'no.'
✓ Develop an understanding of the difference between a healthy relationship and an abusive one.

Materials:

❑ Pens or pencils
❑ *Consider these Questions Early in a Relationship* handout H-23
❑ Journals
❑ Snacks, box of tissues

The Group Session

Opening the Session: Welcome the girls to the group. Reassure them that they cannot fail. Review the group rules. Ask the girls if there is anything from the last session that they would like to talk about or anything from their journal that they would like to share.

Grungie Circle: Review the concept of *grungies* (H-5). Ask each girl to remember a time in the past week when she was 'hit by a *grungie.*' Have each girl retell her story without the *grungie*—replace it with the real feeling.

Session Topic: Relationships with Boys

1. **Why it's Hard to Say No:** Ask the girls to remember a time when they wanted to say no to a boy and didn't. What held them back? Talk about how hard it is to say no. Talk about some of the difficulties girls can get into when they can't say no (for example, having sex when they don't want to, getting into a car with someone who is drunk, etc.).

2. **Saying Yes and No:** This exercise allows girls to use their bodies to practice saying *yes* and *no.* On the count of three have girls clench their fists and jump up into the air. As they come down have them yell 'No!' as loud as they can. Repeat two more times. Do the same exercise having them jump up as high as they can and reach for the ceiling. As they come down, have them yell 'Yes!' as loud as they can. Ask them which is easier for them.

3. **When Relationships are Abusive:** Using H-23 as a guide, talk about the qualities that make relationships healthy and those that make relationships abusive. Talk about what you can do and what supports you will need if you realize that the relationship that you are in is (or might become) abusive.

Closing the Session: Have the girls give each other verbal bouquets.

Session Plan S-17: The Media

[Note: The week before this session, explain the handout *Becoming Media Literate*. Divide the girls into groups of three. Have each group choose a television program to watch and report on.]

Objectives: The girls will...

✓ Practice decoding the *grungies*.
✓ Develop an understanding of how girls and women are portrayed in the media.
✓ Become media literate.

Materials:

❑ Pens or pencils
❑ Poster paper
❑ Magazines, scissors, glue
❑ *Becoming Media Literate* handout H-24
❑ Journals
❑ Snacks, box of tissues

The Group Session

Opening the Session: Welcome the girls to the group. Reassure them that they cannot fail. Review the group rules. Ask the girls if there is anything from the last session that they would like to talk about or anything from their journal that they would like to share.

Grungie Circle: Review the concept of *grungies* (H-5). Ask each girl to remember a time in the past week when she was 'hit by a *grungie*.' Have each girl retell her story without the *grungie* but with the real feeling.

Session Topic: The Media

1. **Becoming Media Literate:** Have each group discuss the television program that they watched. Have them report their findings (handout H-24) to the larger group. Discuss how the media portrays women and girls. What happens if you don't see yourself? How do you feel? If you could change things, what would you do?

2. **Counteracting the Messages of the Media:** Bring in the magazines that you have been collecting. Divide the girls into groups of three. Have one group make a collage of the different ways in which women are portrayed. Have one group make a collage of the 'perfect' woman. Have another group make a collage of the 'realistic' woman. Hang the collages on the wall. Talk about who is included, who is excluded, where each girl fits in. Ask the girls who their heroes are and where they fit in.

Closing the Session: Have the girls give each other verbal bouquets.

Session Plan S-18: Bullying

Objectives: The girls will…

✓ Practice decoding the *grungies*.
✓ Develop understanding of different bullying behaviors.
✓ Have an opportunity to discussion their own experiences of being bullied.
✓ Develop skills and strategies to deal with bullying.

Materials:

❑ Pens or pencils
❑ Journals
❑ Snacks, box of tissues

The Group Session

Opening the Session: Welcome the girls to the group. Reassure them that they cannot fail. Review the group rules. Ask the girls if there is anything from the last session that they would like to talk about or anything from their journal that they would like to share.

Grungie Circle: Review the concept of *grungies* (H-5). Ask each girl to remember a time in the past week when she was 'hit by a *grungie*.' Have each girl retell her story without the grungie but with the real feeling.

Session Topic: Bullying

1. **Talking about Bullying:** Invite the girls to talk about bullying. Let them know that bullying is harmful and that they have the right to come to school and be safe. Encourage the girls to talk about the details: what do people call them, what do they do. Describe the different kinds of bullying behaviors. Talk about girl bullies and boy bullies. Let them know that bullying is about power and has nothing to do with the kind of person that they are.

2. **Strategies to Stay Safe:** Talk about what makes girls feel safe. What can their parents and teachers do to stop bullying? Let the girls know that it takes a whole school to stop bullying but that there are some strategies that can help them as individuals stay safe such as joining activities, finding someone to hang out with, and helping each other. Ask for other suggestions.

3. **Stop! I don't like what you are saying!:** Divide the group into threes. Have one person from each group chose a time when they were bullied. Have the sub-groups act out the scenarios. Each time the *bully* says something, have the *victim* repeat 'Stop, I don't like what you are saying.' (It's tempting to respond to the content, so the *victim* may need support from the third girl who is the coach.)

Closing the Session: Have each girl tell another girl what she appreciates about her. Go around the circle enough times so that every girl receives feedback.

REPRODUCIBLE HANDOUTS

Program facilitators are hereby given permission to reproduce materials contained in this section for free distribution within their groups. You may choose to block out our logo and page numbers.

CONTINUUM OF DISORDERED EATING AND EATING DISORDERS

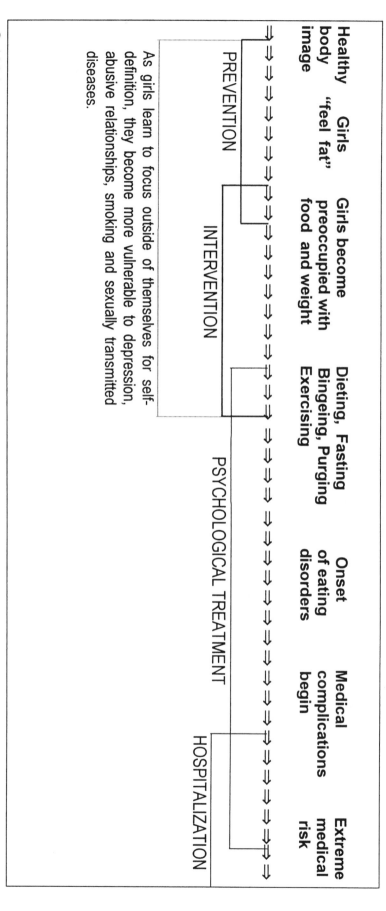

Healthy body image	Girls "feel fat"	Girls become preoccupied with food and weight	Dieting, Fasting Bingeing, Purging Exercising	Onset of eating disorders	Medical complications begin	Extreme medical risk

PREVENTION

INTERVENTION

PSYCHOLOGICAL TREATMENT

HOSPITALIZATION

As girls learn to focus outside of themselves for self-definition, they become more vulnerable to depression, abusive relationships, smoking and sexually transmitted diseases.

INVITING GIRLS TO THE GROUP

Establish Rapport: Use your first name to encourage informality. Tell the girls why you want to run a group for girls, and something about yourself (e.g. I'm a teacher, child and youth worker, a mother with two children, etc.).

Describe the Group: Let the girls know that you are inviting them to a group that deals with their issues and concerns, with "girl talk" and what it is like to grow up as a girl today. Even though the group may be intended for eating disorder prevention, remember that prevention has little to do with the disorders themselves. (I never mention anorexia or bulimia unless I am asked specific questions by the girls.)

Name Their Concerns: You may say something such as 'I remember when I was your age and these were some of the things that I was concerned about,' or 'The girls that I work with that are your age worry about...' Some facilitators role-play these concerns. What you do will depend on your level of comfort. Girls are most likely to participate in a group if the subject is of immediate interest to them. In grades six and seven, girls are concerned with their changing bodies, with friends, teasing, boys, parents and school. In the older grades girls are more concerned with their weight, friends, pleasing other people, relationships, boys, sexuality, pressures to perform in school and wanting more freedom from their parents.

Continuum: Talk about the continuum in the high schools. Tell the girls that this group is not about eating disorders but that they can talk about their concerns with weight if they want to.

Grungies: Talk about the *grungies:* (Use the information in handout H-5 but leave out the practice sessions.)

Encourage Participation: Some girls will feel comfortable participating. Others may have difficulty, especially if the group is large. It helps to give out question cards and pencils before your presentation and to encourage girls to write their questions anonymously.

Invite Girls to the Group: Give each girl information about time, day and location. If you require pre-registration, then give each girl a form to fill out stating whether or not she wants to participate in the group. Have the girls return the form to their teachers (this gives them an opportunity to say no without feeling that they are hurting your feelings).

Involve the Parents: Give each girl a flyer that describes the program and a telephone number where you can be reached for more information and consent form H-3.

Your Organization
letterhead

February 10, 1999

Dear Parents,

[Your Organization], in partnership with Manon Rheaume Elementary School is offering an afternoon discussion group for grade seven girls called *JUST FOR GIRLS*. The program will consist of twelve sessions, each approximately one and one-half hours long. The sessions will be co-facilitated by a trained facilitator from [Your Organization] and by Ms. Gooda Marks, the grade seven teacher at Manon Rheaume Elementary School.

The aim of the *JUST FOR GIRLS* program is to provide girls with the opportunity to talk about issues that may influence their self confidence and self-esteem during adolescence, and to help them develop skills and strategies to combat negative experiences. These experiences often take the form of comments from peers suggesting that they are 'too tall,' 'too skinny,' 'fat,' 'ugly,' 'stupid' and so forth. When girls are upset they often turn these comments against themselves in the form of *grungies*—things that they say to themselves that make them feel badly. While some grade seven girls 'feel stupid,' most of them 'feel fat.' Experiences like these can undermine girls' self-esteem if they are not given a chance to air their concerns and to learn healthy coping skills. It is our hope that by encouraging girls to talk about their concerns we will avert future tendencies towards eating disorders, depression, and substance abuse.

Your daughter has indicated an interest in participating in this group which will be held on Wednesday afternoons from 3:00 to 4:30 at Manon Rheaume Elementary School. The group will begin on Wednesday, February 10 and end on May 5. If you agree to her participation in the group, could you kindly sign the admission form below. If you would like further information about the group, please feel free to contact either myself or Gooda Marks at 555-1234.

Yours truly

Your name   Gooda Marks, teacher
Your Organization   Manon Rheaume Elementary School

I, _____ give permission for my daughter, _____
to attend the *JUST FOR GIRLS* group at Manon Rheaume Elementary School.

Date:_____ Signature:_____

TELL US ABOUT YOU

We are asking you to fill out this form because we would like to know a little about you.

1. Name: _____

2. How old are you? _____ 3. In what grade are you? _____

4. One thing that you like about being a girl today _____

_____

5. One thing that is difficult about being a girl today _____

_____

6. One thing that you like about yourself _____

_____

7. One thing you'd like to change about yourself _____

_____

8. On a scale of 1 - 10, how do you feel about yourself? (circle <u>one</u>)

    1   2   3   4   5   6   7   8   9   10

1 = I feel bad   10 = I feel good
   I don't feel liked   I feel liked, happy, respected
   Everything is going wrong   I feel good about myself
   I don't feel good about who I am inside   I feel good about who I am inside

9. How often do you feel fat?

    A lot   Somewhat   A little   Not at all

10. How often do you feel stupid?

    A lot   Somewhat   A little   Not at all

11. What would you like to learn about in this group?_____

_____

_____

JUST FOR GIRLS

TEACHING GIRLS ABOUT THE GRUNGIES

1. Ask the girls to think about their best friend. Ask them to consider what is it about that person that makes her a best friend. Girls will name qualities such as honesty, good listener, sense of humor, trustworthy, etc. Ask the girls if any of them chose their best friend because she is thin. In a humorous way, ask the girls if they say things to themselves such as 'Jennifer is my best friend. She is thin. I love to go over to her house and watch her thinness. Her thinness is so fascinating.' Their laughter will break the ice.

2. Let girls know that most of us describe our friends in positive ways, yet we don't think that way about ourselves. We don't go around saying, 'I'm so trustworthy. I'm a good friend. I'm a great person.' Usually we think about ourselves in negative terms.

3. Ask how many girls feel fat, ugly or stupid. What other negative things do they say? These things are *grungies*. They are our *negative voice*—the things that we say to ourselves that make us feel badly.

4. Ask the girls what they say when their friends feel fat? Most will tell you they say, 'No, you're not.' What do their friends say? 'Yes I am!' Most girls feel frustrated with this ritual because 'feeling fat' is not a feeling. True feelings allow us to connect with one another and help us share our experiences. When people try to engage with 'feeling fat' they end up frustrated and unheard.

5. Let girls know that when they 'feel fat' (or ugly or stupid, etc.) they are speaking in code. They have been 'hit by a *grungie*' and have to learn the secret of what's underneath in order to understand what they really want to say. If you have had a *grungie* recently use it as an example.

6. Practice decoding the *grungies*. Reassure girls that it takes time to recognize what's underneath.

Decoding the *Grungies*

- Ask the girls to remember when they were 'hit by a *grungie*.'
- Ask them to remember the time of day and what they were doing and feeling at that time.
- Ask the girls to retell the story, this time leaving out the *grungie*.
- Help them identify their real feelings by naming and describing them. For example: 'You must have been feeling insecure. This happens when…'
- Tell them that other girls feel this way.
- Give them a context for their feelings. Explain that the situation is a 'girl thing' or something that happens mainly to girls.
- Help them resolve the issue.

JUST FOR GIRLS
FEEDBACK: *TELL US YOUR OPINIONS*

We are asking you to fill out this form because we would like to know what you think about the *JUST FOR GIRLS* sessions that you have attended. There are no right or wrong answers, and you won't be hurting our feelings telling us what you really think. Your opinions matter to us. Answer as many of the questions as you can. If you run out of room, continue on the other side of this paper.

1. Name: _____

2. How old are you? _____ 3. In what grade are you? _____

4. How many sessions have you attended this time? _____
   (If you don't remember the exact number, circle one of the answers below.)

   All   Almost All   A few   Just one

5. On a scale of 1 - 10, how do you feel about yourself? (circle one)

   1   2   3   4   5   6   7   8   9   10

   1 = I feel bad   10 = I feel good
     I don't feel liked   I feel liked, happy, respected
     Everything is going wrong   I feel good about myself
     I don't feel good about who I am inside   I feel good about who I am inside

6. How often do you feel fat?

   A lot   Somewhat   A little   Not at all

7. How often do you feel stupid?

   A lot   Somewhat   A little   Not at all

8. Do you remember what a *grungie* is? _____ If you do, could you tell us
   what some of your *grungies* are?_____

9. How much was knowing about *grungies* able to help you? (circle one)

   A lot   Somewhat   A little   Not at all

↘

10. Does knowing about *grungies* make you feel any differently about yourself?

Worse   The same   A lttle better   Somewhat better   A lot better

11. What did you like the most about this group? _____

_____

_____

_____

12. What activity or discussion was the most helpful? _____

_____

_____

13. What activity or discussion was the least helpful? _____

_____

_____

14. Have you noticed changes in yourself since you started coming to the group?
_____ If so, can you describe them? _____

_____

_____

15. If you could wish for something else or something different for *JUST FOR GIRLS* what would those things be?_____

_____

_____

Thank You!

BUILDING A HEALTHY SENSE OF SELF

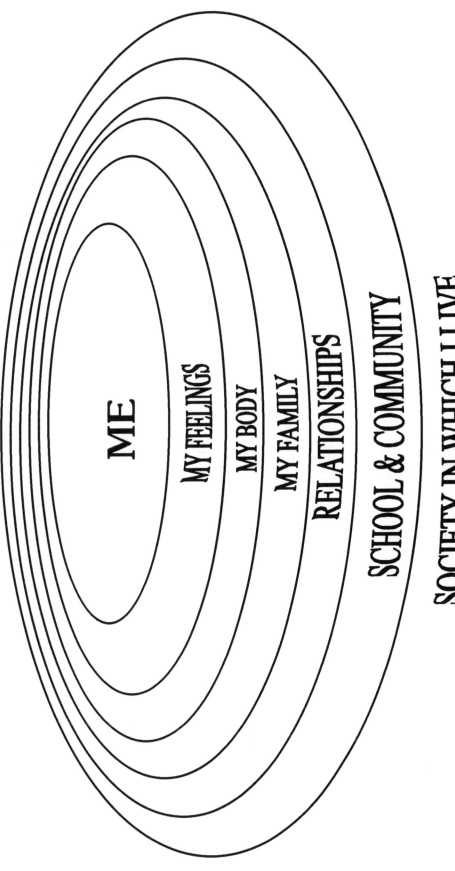

ME

MY FEELINGS

MY BODY

MY FAMILY

RELATIONSHIPS

SCHOOL & COMMUNITY

SOCIETY IN WHICH I LIVE

H-7

JUST FOR GIRLS

VALUING MY PERSONAL STRENGTHS

1. Three things that I value about myself:

_____

_____

_____

2. Three things that make me interesting:

_____

_____

_____

3. Three things that I am good at:

_____

_____

_____

4. Three things that I believe about myself:

_____

_____

_____

5. Three things that are important to me and that I need to make me feel good:

_____

_____

_____

6. My friends can count on me because:

_____

_____

_____

H-9   *JUST FOR GIRLS*

BUILDING A FEELING VOCABULARY

Adapted from *Feed Your Head: Some Excellent Stuff on Being Yourself* by Earl Hipp (Minneapolis: Hazeldon, 1991)

Feel free to add to or subtract from this list...

afraid	alone	annoyed	amused	awful
awesome	bitter	belittled	bored	confused
concerned	crabby	calm	cautious	content
disappointed	defeated	discouraged	eager	elated
enthusiastic	encouraged	enraged	excited	excluded
fearful	funny	furious	frustrated	great
gullible	glad	hopeful	hurt	hollow
hopeless	insecure	irritated	inadequate	included
insecure	joyful	jealous	lonely	lost
mad	mushy	miserable	messed up	mindless
needy	nervous	overwhelmed	open	optimistic
paranoid	powerful	pent up	pushed	powerless
rejected	resentful	respected	sad	scared
safe	self-conscious	silly	shamed	shallow
spaced out	surprised	tense	terrible	threatened
tolerant	unloved	unsure	unimportant	validated
valued	victimized	wanted	worried	

PLAYING FEELING CHARADES

Cut out the boxes and separate into piles
according to the level of difficulty:

RELATIVELY EASY	MODERATELY DIFFICULT	DIFFICULT
Happy	Proud	Comforted
Silly	Curious	Insecure
Sick	Disappointed	Sorry
Mad	Bored	Lonely
Scared	Worried	Jealous
Sad	Surprised	Numb
Tired	Embarrassed	Criticized
Frustrated	Hurt	Rejected
Excited	Open	Powerless

JUST FOR GIRLS

HOW I FEEL ABOUT MY BODY

1. My first memory of a positive body image or of feeling really good about my body:

_____

_____

2. My first memory of a negative body image or of feeling really badly about my body:

_____

_____

3. The media influences how I feel about my body by:

_____

_____

4. My friends influence how I feel about my body by:

_____

_____

5. My family influences how I feel about my body by:

_____

_____

6. If I had an ideal body my life would be different because:

_____

_____

7. If I had to rank how I feel about my body today, it would be: (circle a number)

1   2   3   4   5   6   7   8   9   10

  Love   *Hate*

8. I feel this way: (choose <u>one</u>)

    Always   Sometimes   Just once in a while

EXPLORING YOUR EATING HABITS

1. Have you ever eaten when you are not hungry? Give two examples. _____

   _____

2. Do you like to eat alone or with others? Why? _____

   _____

3. What foods do you eat that are influenced by:

   a. Your religious beliefs or customs? _____

   _____

   b. Your friends? _____

   _____

   c. Advertising? _____

   _____

   d. Special occasions? _____

   _____

Sometimes certain feelings want to make us eat certain things.
What kinds of food do you eat when you are :

Feeling:	Examples of Foods:
Happy	
Bored	
Tired	
Angry	
Excited	
Lonely	
Nervous	
Insecure	

JUST FOR GIRLS

EXPLORING THE MYTHS ABOUT DIETING

Adapted from Teacher's Resource Kit from National Eating Disorder Information Centre, Toronto

True or False?

Read each statement. Check the box that you think is correct:

True? False?

True?	False?	
		1. Dieting always leads to permanent weight loss.
		2. Each person has their own natural weight.
		3. It's easy to lose weight!
		4. People are fat because they overeat.
		5. All fat people are unhealthy.
		6. Thin people are healthier than fat people.
		7. Eating normally means eating only diet foods.
		8. Dieting may cause weight gain.
		9. Most diets don't work.
		10. Normal eating means eating a variety of foods.
		11. It's easy for everyone to gain weight.
		12. Everyone can change their body shape if they try hard.
		13. Dieting can lead to an eating disorder.
		14. Dieting can make a person unhealthy.

WHAT *REALLY* HAPPENS WHEN WE DIET

Adapted from material provided by *British Columbia Ministry of Health and Ministry Responsible for Seniors*

HOW **WE DIET**	**THIS IS WHAT** *REALLY* **HAPPENS**
Skipping meals or decreasing calories	√ This lowers metabolism so we store fat more easily from fewer calories. √ The brain's and muscle's demand for fuel causes rebound 'munchies, usually for high fat and high sugar items. √ Poor attention span, irritability, fatigue. √ Muscle tissue may be lost.
Cut out starchy foods	√ Your body loses its best source of stable energy. You'll be more likely to feel moody and tired. √ You'll end up eating higher fat and sugary foods to satisfy munchies.
Cut out meats without Comparable replacement	√ May risk iron deficiency which leads to fatigue. √ Energy from meals may not last as long, causing more hunger between meals for high fat, high sugar foods.
Go on preplanned meal replacement diet or liquid diet	√ You have a 95% chance of regaining any weight you lose in 1 to 2 years. √ You give away control to the plan, which lowers your self-esteem. √ You often lose muscle mass along with fat. This lowers your metabolism, making it easier to store fat on fewer calories. √ Habits are replaced temporarily, not changed permanently. Also, it's expensive.
Fasting	√ Most of the weight lost is water. √ Muscle mass decreases—which lowers metabolism. Subsequent fat gain. √ Can be medically dangerous for some individuals.

WHY **WE DIET**	**THIS IS WHAT** *REALLY* **HAPPENS**
To be slim	√ Slimness is temporary. Over the long run, 95% of dieters regain the weight. Many women get fatter, so they diet again, with similar poor results. This is called *diet cycling* and it can lead to obesity.
To be healthier	√ *Diet cycling* increases health risks more than being overweight. √ There is no evidence that being plump is unhealthy. There *is* evidence to show that being too slim is unhealthy. √ Most dieting decreases our muscle mass. Muscles are needed for good health. √ Many diets are unhealthy. Your body and mind don't run well when you restrict calories. Dieting makes you moody and irritable, and makes you obsessed with food. This feels like failure, but in fact it is a physiological response and has nothing to do with will power.
To be more attractive	√ What attracts you to someone else? Do you want your friends to like you for your body or yourself? What are long term relationships based upon? If you are dieting, are you any fun to be around?

JUST FOR GIRLS 🦎

MAKING ASSERTIVE STATEMENTS

As a group, decide upon an assertive response for each of the following situations.
Have one person write down your response on your sheet.
Be prepared to act them out.

1. Your brother is using the telephone but you need to call someone very soon.

2. You have been standing in line for hours to buy tickets for a concert and someone tries to push ahead of you.

3. Your best friend is playing in a hockey tournament after school. Your teacher wants you to stay and help her but you want to go and cheer for your friend.

4. Your boyfriend / girl friend wants to go to a movie that you don't want to see.

5. You are feeling upset and your friend is bugging you to tell her what is wrong. You just want time for yourself.

6. Your friends try to encourage you to have a party at your house when your parents are away even though you promised not to.

7. One of your male friends is thinking of taking family studies and his friends are teasing him about it.

8. A boy in your class keeps asking you out. You do not want to go out with him.

9. A friend whom you occasionally give hugs to extends his greeting too long. He stands with his arm around you talking to other people.

10. Your teacher puts you together with a group of boys to work on a project. You do not want to be in their group because they horse around and never get anything done.

RESPONDING ASSERTIVELY TO SITUATIONS

Cut apart the following scenarios and hand them out separately to the
different groups. Have each group act out a different scenario.
After each performance, encourage the audience to talk
about how they would have handled the situation.

1. You have just come home from school, and you have promised a friend you will go
to the store with her. Your mother insists that you stay home and wash dishes.

2. You are with a group of three girls. You would really like to play basketball but,
as usual, everyone wants to go to the mall.

3. Your father told your sister to rake the back yard. Your sister ran out the door,
so your father made you do it. Your sister has now come home.

4. You are the only friend that Sarah has. You have spent the day at school talking and
joking with Amy. At the end of the day, Sarah walks by you and calls you a bitch.

5. You have just begun to do the dishes. Your father is in the next room watching
TV. A friend comes by and invites you to the pool. Her family will be leaving
in 10 minutes.

6. Last night your mom and dad had a big fight. You were so sad and scared that
you forgot to do your homework. Your teacher yelled at you and called you
lazy in front of the whole class.

7. Your borrowed your mother's earrings without asking. She sees you with them
on and starts yelling.

8. You go to a movie with a boy. He wants to kiss you but you want to watch the movie.

9. You left your composition on the kitchen table for your dad to read when he came
home. He has corrected your spelling and changed some of your sentences.

JUST FOR GIRLS 🐉

TELLING SOMEONE HOW THEIR BEHAVIOR MAKES YOU FEEL

Cut apart the following scenarios and hand them out separately to the
different groups. Have each group act out a different scenario.
After each performance, encourage the audience to talk
about how they would have handled the situation.

1. Your sister keeps borrowing your clothes without asking you. When you try to tell her how you feel she becomes defensive and accuses you of being selfish.

2. Every time that you want to go out with your friends your mother makes you take your younger brother with you.

3. Your father wants you to do well in school. He never tells you that you are doing well. Instead he makes changes in your compositions or corrects your spelling.

4. Your best friend tells the boy that you secretly like that you like him.

5. Every time that you make arrangements to go out with your boyfriend, he is late.

6. A girl in your class is telling secrets about you.

7. The woman at the corner store is always rude to adolescents. You want to keep going there because it is close to your school but don't like her behavior.

8. Every time that you raise your hand in class it seems as if your teacher calls on one of the boys instead.

9. You feel that your best friend never listens to you. She always wants to talk about herself.

10. Your friend is always talking about feeling fat. It's getting boring.

RULES FOR GOOD COMMUNICATION AND FOR FIGHTING FAIRLY

» Identify the Problem

» Define the Problem as a Mutual One

» Attack the Problem not the Person

» Don't Make Assumptions about the Other Person

» Check Out Your Perceptions

» Practice 'I' Messages

» Listen with an Open Mind

» Stay with the Specific Issue

» Avoid Generalizations such as 'You always!' or 'You never!'

» Avoid Name-calling, Blaming, Putting the Other Person Down

» Treat the Other Person with Respect

JUST FOR GIRLS

ALL KINDS OF FAMILIES

Adapted from *Straight Talk about Parents* by Elizabeth A. Ryan

There are all kinds of families. No one kind is 'normal' or better than another. You may know someone or you may belong to a family like one of the following:

The father goes to work each day and the mother stays and looks after the children and the home. Even though this is the kind of family that we see in movies, books and on television, surveys and statistics show that most people do not live in this type of family.

In some families, the mother works outside the home and the father stays at home and raises the children.

The mother or father is raising the children in a single parent home because the other parent is dead, is very sick, or lives far away from the children.

The parents are divorced and the children live with one of the parents and visit the other on weekends or every other week.

The parents are divorced and the children live with the mother part of the time and with the father an equal part of the time.

Children live in families with one natural parent, one step-parent and brothers and sisters.

Children live in blended families with one natural parent, one step-parent and with each parent's children as well as the children that they may have together.

Children may live with parents who have adopted them.

Children may live with foster parents who are caring for them.

Children may live with a parent some of the time and with a relative some of the time.

Sometimes one child may live at home while another child lives with a relative or in a hospital or with friends of the family.

Families may be made up of children who live with grandparents, aunts, uncles or other relatives and/or friends.

In some families, a grandparent or aunt or uncle lives with the family.

Sometimes families are made up of two women or two men who are living together and raising children together.

BEST FRIENDS

Here is an opportunity for you to learn about what makes someone your best friend. There are no right answers or wrong answers. If you can't answer some of the questions, then leave them out and come back to them later—maybe even tomorrow or next week. The group discussion may help you think of things that you missed.

1. Who is your best friend? _____

2. How did you meet and become best friends? _____

3. What is the best part of having a best friend? _____

4. What is the hardest part of having a best friend? _____

5. What are the similarities between you? _____

_____

6. What are the differences between you? _____

_____

7. What interests do you share? _____

_____

8. What do you disagree about? _____

_____

9. What are three qualities that drew you to her? _____

_____

10. What are three things about her that bug you? _____

_____

11. What are some of the problems that you have with your friend? _____

_____

12. How do you resolve them? _____

_____

JUST FOR GIRLS

CHOOSING A PARTNER

Choose someone that you are interested in.
(You can change your mind and be interested in someone else tomorrow!)

1. What are some of the things that this person likes? _____

2. What are some of this person's dislikes? _____

3. What kind of personality does this person have? _____

4. What kind of person is this person? _____

5. How are you alike? _____

_____

6. How are you different? _____

_____

7. Describe the 'ideal' partner. _____

_____

8. How would this person make you feel? _____

_____

9. How would you get along with one another? _____

_____

10. What kinds of things would you do together? _____

11. How would you want this person to treat you? _____

_____

12. How would you want this person to make you feel? _____

_____

13. How would you want this person to be with your friends? _____

_____

CONSIDER THESE QUESTIONS *EARLY* IN A RELATIONSHIP

Adapted from Canadian Red Cross: *Dating Violence Prevention*

HOW DO I KNOW IF SOMEONE LOVES ME?
...Is this person I care about someone who:

- listens to me?
- considers my feelings and ideas?
- shares my interests, activities and beliefs?
- enjoys spending time with me?
- remembers little things that are important to me?
- lets me be first sometimes?
- values and takes care of himself?
- does everything he can to help me reach my full potential?

HOW DO I KNOW IF SOMEONE COULD HURT ME?
...Is this person I care about someone who:

- ignores my feelings and wishes?
- teases and ridicules me about things that are important to me?
- doesn't keep my confidences?
- ignores me or pretends not to hear me?
- acts more friendly when we are alone than when his friends are around?
- encourages or pressures me to do things that make me uncomfortable?
- sulks when I don't do what he wants?
- often shows anger and uses threats or violence to get his own way?

JUST FOR GIRLS

BECOMING MEDIA LITERATE

When we watch television or read magazines or newspapers, it is important to be able to look at them critically in order to understand the messages that they trying to give us. Choose a television show that you really like. As you watch it, answer the questions listed below. You might have to watch the show more than once.

1. What is the name of the show?

2. What is the show about?

3. Who are the main characters?

4. What does the male character tell us about how men are supposed to be?

5. What does the female character tell us about how women are supposed to be?

6. What messages does the show give us about being male and being female?

7. What images about body image and what standard of beauty do the characters in this show reflect?

8. Does the show include any characters of different races?

9. If so, how are they portrayed?

10. Does the show include any characters who are fat or disabled?

11. If so, how are they portrayed?

12. If you were the director, how would you portray the women in the show?

13. If you were the director, how would your show include a wide range of people?

INFORMATION ABOUT STEROIDS

Adapted from Canadian Centre for Ethics in Sport: *The Steroids and Body Image Project*

Warning Signs...
Someone who is using steroids may have the following symptoms:
- ✓ Swollen or puffy face—caused by excessive water retention.
- ✓ Severe acne—especially on the back, shoulders and chest.
- ✓ Rapid weight gain—between 8–20 lbs. in the first 6 to 8 weeks of use.
- ✓ Personality changes—increased aggression, mood swings and irritability.
- ✓ Jaundice—the eyes and skin may become yellow.
- ✓ Premature hair loss or thinning.
- ✓ Obsession with body image and with food and weight.

Physical Side Effects:
- ✓ Persistent headaches, nosebleeds and stomach aches.
- ✓ Severe acne—especially on the back, shoulders and chest.
- ✓ Hair loss.
- ✓ Breast enlargement.
- ✓ Shrunken testicles and lowered sperm count which may lead to sterility and impotence.
- ✓ Damage to liver and kidneys.
- ✓ High blood pressure and increased cholesterol levels which may lead to heart disease.
- ✓ Premature fusion of the long bones, which may lead to stunted growth.

Psychological Side Effects:
- ✓ Increased aggressiveness and bursts of anger—also known as 'Roid rage.'
- ✓ Frequent and severe mood swings.
- ✓ Paranoia, sometimes leading to violence.

Higher risk of Hepatitis B and C, and HIV (AIDS)
- ✓ Steroids can be taken orally or by injection. Anyone who shares needles or vials is at risk of contracting diseases such as hepatitis B and C and HIV, the virus that causes AIDS.

JUST FOR GIRLS

Also by Sandra Susan Friedman and available from *Salal Books*:

WHEN GIRLS FEEL FAT
Helping Girls Through Adolescence

Toronto: HarperCollins, 1997   trade paperback
ISBN# 0-00-638561-3   246 pages $20.00

When Girls Feel Fat helps parents and their daughters to understand and cope with the difficult process of adolescence. Sandra Friedman's friendly guide demystifies the relationships that girls have with body image, friends, parents, sexuality, eating disorders, school and the media. She explains that *feeling fat* provides a key to opening discussion about what happens to girls growing up female in a male world—a process that puts tremendous pressure on girls to grow up to be 'perfect,' to be accepted by others and still remain true to themselves. Through case notes from her private practice and discussion groups, and feedback from the *GIRLS IN THE 90S / JUST FOR GIRLS* programs, the author draws upon a wealth of useful experiences and coping techniques.

When Girls Feel Fat gives parents, teachers and professionals who work with girls empathetic, clear, and proven strategies to deal with adolescent conflict, to recognize that worries about weight can lead to serious eating disorders, to maintain a connection in the face of girls 'tuning out,' and to cope with the *grungies*—Sandra's term for the voice of girls' self-deprecating negative feelings.

FUND RAISERS: If your organization sells resource materials to the public, maintains a book table at conferences, or needs a unique product for door-to-door solicitation, *When Girls Feel Fat* is available at an attractive discount in quantity. Contact *Salal Books* for bulk-purchase pricing and conditions.

Please photocopy this order form.
Payment by personal check or money order.
Government and institutional purchase orders are welcomed.

SALAL BOOKS
#309, 101-1184 Denman Street
Vancouver, BC, Canada V6G 2M9
☎ + 🖷 604-689-8399

_____ x *JUST FOR GIRLS*   @ $35 = _____.____

_____ x *WHEN GIRLS FEEL FAT* @ $20 = _____.____

Shipping & handling @ $3/book = _____.____

Canadian customers: calculate GST 7% (or HST 15%) + _____

❏ GST exempt R-_____   TOTAL: $ _____.____

Please include your complete mailing address and telephone number with your order.